Reasoning and Writing

Level C
Writing Extensions

A Division of The McGraw·Hill Companies
Columbus, Ohio

Cover Credits

(t) ©SuperStock, (b) Animal Graphics.

Illustration Credit

Susan Jerde

SRA/McGraw-Hill

A Division of The **McGraw-Hill** *Companies*

Send all inquiries to:
SRA/McGraw-Hill
4400 Easton Commons
Columbus, OH 43219

Printed in the United States of America.

ISBN 0-02-684777-9

7 8 9 PBM 07

Contents

Introduction

Writing Extensions, Level C

The writing extensions for the third-grade level of *Reasoning and Writing* consist of 90 scripted lessons (lessons 1–90 in this book) and 67 blackline masters (BLMs) for specified lessons.

Objectives

The general objective of the grade-three extensions is to give students opportunities to apply what they have learned about writing to a wider variety of contexts. Students should be able to write the various essays that the extensions present with a minimum of additional teaching or preparation. In addition to the activities specified for extensions, you may assign students additional assignments that require them to compare and contrast. You could design these assignments so they follow the same format as the assignments presented in the extension.

The work on less-structured assignments also prepares the students for tests that require writing and that give students only general directions.

Scheduling the Extension Activities

Each extension lesson takes 15–30 minutes. Start the extensions by presenting lesson 1 and presenting the lessons in order. The sequence may begin after the students have completed lesson 51 in *Reasoning and Writing,* Level C. **Do not delay beginning the sequence beyond lesson 60 in the regular program.**

Note that the extension activities should not replace any regular lessons in *Reasoning and Writing.* Ideally, the extension activities would be presented at another time of day.

If students are quite firm on the particular extension activity, you may present it as homework or present more than one activity as part of a daily assignment.

Using the Teacher Presentation Scripts

The script conventions for the extension lessons are the same as those for *Reasoning and Writing.* The teaching practices are also the same. For information about these practices, refer to the Teacher's Guide for *Reasoning and Writing,* Level C.

Procedures for Presenting Extension Activities

The lessons that require blackline masters are listed on page 143. A reminder at the beginning of each of these lessons indicates that a blackline master is needed. The number of each blackline master corresponds to the number of the extension activity. For extension 42, BLM 42 is presented. Because there are some lessons that do not require a blackline master, the numbering of the blackline masters is not consecutive. There are no blackline masters for Extension lessons 39 through 41, for instance, because these lessons do not require a blackline master.

Content

The extensions cover the following writing skills:

- Alphabetizing-and-reference skills
- Passage Writing:
  - Inferring missing content from picture sequences
  - Writing based on vague pictures
  - Retelling
  - Writing endings to stories
  - Topics that involve personal experiences
- Writing directions for making figures
- Writing poems

Tracks

Alphabetizing-and-Reference Skills

Starting with extension lesson 11, students alphabetize lists of words, use guide words to sort entries (show which words or topics would be found on a particular page) and refer to a dictionary to discover what specific words mean in specific contexts. BLMs accompany all of the activities except those from lessons 39–41 (using a dictionary).

Here's an example of an early activity from lesson 11.

BLM 11

Use the words below to make an alphabetical list.

great
carrot
top
horse
right
visit
elephant
north
jail
million

1. ____
2. ____
3. ____
4. ____
5. ____
6. ____
7. ____
8. ____
9. ____
10. ____

154

Students write the list of words in alphabetical order.

After students have learned guide words, they use the guide words to determine which words would appear on a page of a reference book.

Here is an example from lesson 34.

BLM 34

cent **cops**

can
certain
cup
chip
circus
clipper
call
city

1. ____
2. ____
3. ____
4. ____
5. ____

177

Students identify which of the 8 words would go on the page and then write these words in alphabetical order.

On some lessons, students refer to their glossary to determine the first entry that would appear on the page and the last entry for that page.

Here's an example from lesson 36.

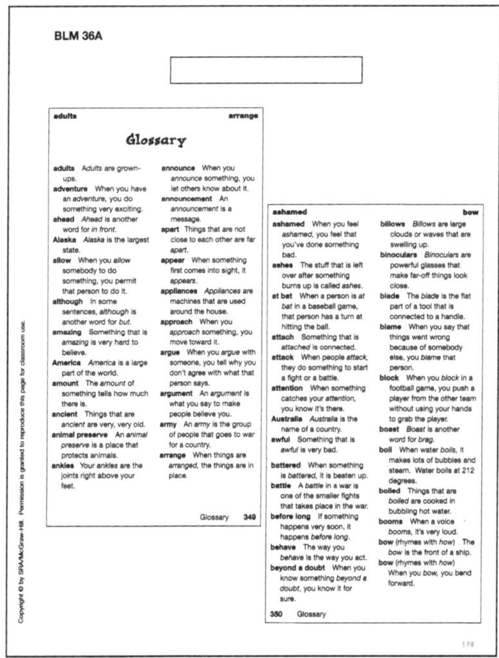

BLM 36A

adults **arrange**

Glossary

adults *Adults* are grown-ups.
adventure When you have an *adventure*, you do something very exciting.
ahead *Ahead* is another word for *in front*.
Alaska *Alaska* is the largest state.
allow When you *allow* somebody to do something, you permit that person to do it.
although In some sentences, *although* is another word for *but*.
amazing Something that is *amazing* is very hard to believe.
America *America* is a large part of the world.
amount The *amount* of something tells how much there is.
ancient Things that are *ancient* are very, very old.
animal preserve An *animal preserve* is a place that protects animals.
ankles Your *ankles* are the joints right above your feet.
announce When you *announce* something, you let others know about it.
announcement An *announcement* is a message.
apart Things that are not close to each other are far *apart*.
appear When something first comes into sight, it *appears*.
appliances *Appliances* are machines that are used around the house.
approach When you *approach* something, you move toward it.
argue When you *argue* with someone, you tell why you don't agree with what that person says.
argument An *argument* is what you say to make people believe you.
army An *army* is the group of people that goes to war for a country.
arrange When things are *arranged*, the things are in place.

Glossary 349

ashamed **bow**

ashamed When you feel *ashamed*, you feel that you've done something bad.
ashes The stuff that is left over after something burns up is called *ashes*.
at bat When a person is *at bat* in a baseball game, that person has a turn at hitting the ball.
attach Something that is *attached* is connected.
attack When people *attack*, they do something to start a fight or a battle.
attention When something catches your *attention*, you know it's there.
Australia *Australia* is the name of a country.
awful Something that is *awful* is very bad.
battered When something is *battered*, it is beaten up.
battle A *battle* in a war is one of the smaller fights that takes place in the war.
before long If something happens very soon, it happens *before long*.
behave The way you *behave* is the way you act.
beyond a doubt When you know something *beyond a doubt*, you know it for sure.
billows *Billows* are large clouds or waves that are swelling up.
binoculars *Binoculars* are powerful glasses that make far-off things look close.
blade The *blade* is the flat part of a tool that is connected to a handle.
blame When you say that things went wrong because of somebody else, you *blame* that person.
block When you *block* in a football game, you push a player from the other team without using your hands to grab the player.
boast *Boast* is another word for *brag*.
boil When water *boils*, it makes lots of bubbles and steam. Water boils at 212 degrees.
boiled Things that are *boiled* are cooked in bubbling hot water.
booms When a voice *booms*, it's very loud.
bow (rhymes with *how*) The *bow* is the front of a ship.
bow (rhymes with *how*) When you *bow*, you bend forward.

350 Glossary

179

1. (Hand out sample glossaries to the students [BLM 36A].)
- These are glossaries from the back of a textbook. You'll use glossaries to find words and do other exercises.
- Find page 349 in your glossary. A glossary gives meanings of words that are used in a book. The words are in alphabetical order. The two words at the top of each page are called guide words.

2. The first guide word on page 349 is **adults.** Everybody, touch that guide word. ✔
- That tells that the first word on page 349 is **adults.**
- Touch the other guide word for page 349. ✔
- Everybody, what's that guide word? (Signal.) *Arrange.*
- That tells that the last word on page 349 is **arrange.**

3. Find page 350. ✔
- Page 350 has two guide words. Everybody, touch the first guide word on that page. ✔
- What's the first guide word? (Signal.) *Ashamed.*
- So what's the first word on page 350? (Signal.) *Ashamed.*
- What's the second guide word on page 350? (Call on a student. Accept *bow̆* or *bōw*.)
- Everybody, so what's the last word on that page? (Signal.) *Bow.*

4. (Write on the board:)

asteroid

- Let's say I want to add the word **asteroid** to the glossary. Would I add **asteroid** to page 349 or to page 350? (Wait.) What page? (Signal.) *350.*
- Yes, **asteroid** comes between **ashamed** and **bow** in the alphabet.

5. Your turn. Copy the word **asteroid.** Write it in the box at the top of your worksheet. ✔
- Now draw an arrow to show where the word **asteroid** would go in the glossary. Draw that arrow between two words. Raise your hand when you're finished. (Observe students and give feedback.)
- Everybody, name the word that comes just before where **asteroid** goes. (Signal.) *Ashes.*
- Yes, **asteroid** comes between **ashes** and **at bat** in the alphabet.

Passage Writing: Inference

Starting with lesson 1, students describe specific parts of pictures that show a "before-after" sequence.

Here's an example from lesson 1.

The students write a sentence about the cat in picture 1 and the cat in picture 2. Students then write about the glass in picture 1 and the glass in picture 2. Students use their own lined paper.

Starting with lesson 6, students work with the same set of pictures, but this time, they use information about the differences between the first picture and the second picture to tell what must have happened after the first picture but before the second picture. They start by identifying what is different in each picture. Each element that is different implies something that must have happened between the pictures. Students write four or more sentences that describe the events that occurred in the missing middle picture.

Here is the exercise from extension lesson 6.

BLM 6

Write four or more sentences that tell about everything that must have happened in the middle picture. Remember, tell about **the boy, the glass, the milk** and **the cat.**

1.

2.

3.

floor boy's hand spilled dropped paper towels

1. (Hand out BLM 6.)
- You've told about pictures 1 and 3 before. This time, you're going to write about what happened in the middle picture. That's picture 2.

2. Touch something that is different in pictures 1 and 3. ✔
- Name something that is different in pictures 1 and 3. (Call on different students. Ideas: *Milk, boy, glass, floor, cat, paper towels.*)
- I'll name everything that's different in the pictures: the boy, the glass, the milk, the cat, the floor, the paper towels.
- Your turn. Name the things that are different. (Call on different students. Ideas: *The boy, the glass, the milk, the cat, the floor, the paper towels.*)

3. Listen: You're going to tell me about everything that happened to make picture 3 different. You have to tell me about **the boy, the glass, the milk** and **the cat.** What are you going to tell me about? (Signal.) *The boy, the glass, the milk and the cat.*
- Tell me what the boy must have done. (Call on a student. Ideas: *The boy dropped the glass. The boy went over to the paper towels.*)
- Tell me what happened to the glass. (Call on a student. Idea: *The glass fell on the floor.*)
- Tell me what happened to the milk. (Call on a student. Idea: *The milk spilled on the floor.*)
- Tell me what the cat did. (Call on a student. Idea: *The cat went over to the spilled milk.*)

4. Who can tell me everything that happened? (Call on different students. Praise accounts that tell about the boy, the glass, the milk and the cat.)

5. Your turn. Use lined paper. Write four or more sentences that tell about everything that must have happened in the middle picture. Remember, tell about the boy, the glass, the milk and the cat. Pencils down when you're finished.
(Observe students and give feedback.)
- (Call on different students to read their accounts. Praise parts that are good. Offer suggestions for parts that are not clear or that are missing.)

Passage Writing: Vague Pictures

These activities start on lesson 59. A BLM accompanies each activity. The BLM presents a vague picture that suggests a mood and some details. Here's the picture for extension lesson 84.

You tell the students simply to write about what happened before the picture, what's happening in the picture, what the characters are thinking and feeling and what the outcome will be. You encourage them to make the story interesting. They are to use the skills that they have learned to create a story. After students complete their passage, different students read their stories to the group. Remember, for this activity students are pretty much on their own. If they ask about what they **should** say, respond by telling them that different people see different things in these pictures. The student should write about what the picture suggests and make it interesting.

Students usually write very good accounts. After they complete the sequence of extension activities, you may want to present writing assignments with other vague pictures.

Retelling

The extension presents seven retelling activities, starting at lesson 55. No BLMs accompany the retelling activities. Students listen to an oral passage of about 100 words that you read to them twice. Next, individual students retell the passage orally. Next, students write the passage with as much detail as they are able to recall. Finally, different students read their accounts and receive feedback.

Students hand in their passages. After you mark mistakes, omissions and other major problems, you return the papers, and students rewrite their account from the beginning. Note that you may have to present the oral version of the account again before students write their final draft.

Here's a retell exercise from lesson 55.

EXERCISE A

RETELLING

1. I'll tell a story twice. Then I'll call on different students to tell parts of the story. Remember the story well, because you're going to write it after we tell it.

- Listen big:

> Ricky read a very long book about a jewel robbery. Somebody stole jewels that were worth more than one million dollars. A policeman tried to find out who the robber was. The book was very exciting. At last Ricky came to the part that told who robbed the jewels, but the last page of the book was missing.
>
> Ricky looked and looked for the missing page but he couldn't find it. So he called his friend Lilly. She had read the book and told him that the jewel robber was the grandmother.

- Listen to the story again:

> Ricky read a very long book about a jewel robbery. Somebody stole jewels that were worth more than one million dollars. A policeman tried to find out who the robber was. The book was very exciting. At last Ricky came to the part that told who robbed the jewels, but the last page of the book was missing.
>
> Ricky looked and looked for the missing page but he couldn't find it. So he called his friend Lilly. She had read the book and told him that the jewel robber was the grandmother.

2. Here's the first sentence of the story: **Ricky read a very long book about a jewel robbery.**
- Everybody, say that sentence. (Signal.) *Ricky read a very long book about a jewel robbery.*
3. Start with the words **somebody stole jewels that were worth** . . . and tell what they were worth and who was trying to find the robber. (Call on different students. Idea: *Somebody stole jewels that were worth one million dollars. A policeman tried to find out who the robber was.*)
- Tell what happened when Ricky came to the part that told who robbed the jewels. (Call on different students. Ideas: *The last page of the book was missing. Ricky looked and looked for the missing page.*)
- Tell what Ricky did to find out who stole the jewels and tell who was the robber. (Call on different students. Ideas: *He called his friend Lilly, who had read the book. She told him that the robber was the grandmother.*)
4. I'll tell the whole story one more time:

> Ricky read a very long book about a jewel robbery. Somebody stole jewels that were worth more than one million dollars. A policeman tried to find out who the robber was. The book was very exciting. At last Ricky came to the part that told who robbed the jewels, but the last page of the book was missing.
>
> Ricky looked and looked for the missing page but he couldn't find it. So he called his friend Lilly. She had read the book and told him that the jewel robber was the grandmother.

5. (Call on different students to tell the whole story. Praise accounts that have most of the detail. For parts that are left out, ask other students:) Who can tell me about an important part that was left out of that story?
6. Everybody, you're going to write the whole story. Write it just the way you heard it. Raise your hand when you're finished.
   (Observe students and give feedback.)
- (Call on different students to read the whole story. Praise accounts that have most of the detail. For parts that are left out, ask other students:) Who can tell me an important part that was left out of that story?
7. (Collect papers. Mark errors in clarity, spelling and punctuation. During the next language period, pass back the corrected papers and present Exercise B.)

EXERCISE B

REWRITING

- (Return corrected papers to students.)
- You did a good job the first time you wrote about Ricky. Now you're going to write a perfect paper. Rewrite the whole story from the beginning. Write it so it doesn't have any mistakes.

- (After students complete their final draft, post the papers [and illustrations] of the story.)

The ability to retell an account so that it retains a great amount of detail provided by the original is one of the most important skills that a young writer can learn. It forges the relationship between listening, speaking and writing. It gives the students practice in listening to something that is spoken and then reproducing it, not as spoken words but as a written account. The more sensitive students are to providing accurate retelling, the more potential they have to learn more about writing from what they read and what they hear.

Writing Endings

These activities are similar to the retell except you tell the first **part** of a story. Students write that part. Then they make up an ending.

Here's the activity from lesson 75.

1. I'll tell the first part of a story. Then you'll write the part I tell and the ending to the story.
   - Listen carefully so that you can tell the story the same way I tell it:

A dog and a cat were friends. One day the dog and the cat were walking along when the cat fell into a deep hole. The cat could not get out of the hole. The dog barked and scratched around, but it did not know how to get the cat out of the hole.

   - Listen to that part again:

A dog and a cat were friends. One day the dog and the cat were walking along when the cat fell into a deep hole. The cat could not get out of the hole. The dog barked and scratched around, but it did not know how to get the cat out of the hole.

2. Here's the first sentence in the story: **A dog and a cat were friends.**
   - Everybody, say that sentence. (Signal.) *A dog and a cat were friends.*
   - Listen: One day the dog and the cat were doing something when something happened. Start with the words **one day** and say the sentence from the story. (Call on a student. Praise close approximations: *One day the dog and the cat were walking along when the cat fell into a deep hole.*)
3. (Call on different students to retell the entire first part. Praise accounts that have most of the detail. For parts that are left out, ask other students:) Who can tell me about an important part that was left out of the story?
4. Everybody, you're going to write the whole story. Start out by writing the first part just the way you heard it. Raise your hand when you've done that much. (Observe students and give feedback.)
   - (Call on different students to read the first part. Praise and correct.)
5. Now you're going to write an ending that tells how the dog helped the cat get out of the hole. Maybe the dog got someone to help. Maybe the dog figured out what to drop into the hole.
   - Everybody, write your ending. Raise your hand when you're finished. (Observe students and give feedback.)
6. (Call on different students to read their ending. Praise good plans.)
7. (Collect papers. Mark errors in clarity, spelling and punctuation.)

Topics

There are 16 topics. BLMs accompany 9 of them. For the remaining 7, prompts are presented only on the chalkboard.

Students write about topics that are related to their personal experiences and preferences—somebody I would like to know better, what I did in school yesterday, a time somebody helped me out, my favorite

TV show, someone I really admire, a time I helped somebody. Students write as many paragraphs as they need to complete their accounts.

The topics are sequenced so that students first work on variations of a topic that are prompted by BLMs. Later, they do similar topics that are not prompted. For many of these topics, the student has to indicate a preference and then provide examples and anecdotes to support the choice. For instance, students have to identify a job they would someday like to have.

For some applications, students make numbered lists. For example, when they write about "My Best Friend," they make a list of three things that they really like about that person.

Here's the BLM from lesson 65.

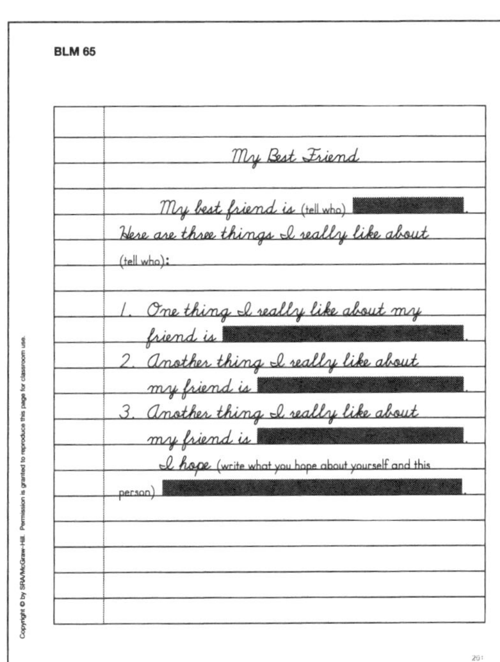

BLM 65

My Best Friend

My best friend is (tell who) ___.
Here are three things I really like about (tell who):

1. One thing I really like about my friend is ___.
2. Another thing I really like about my friend is ___.
3. Another thing I really like about my friend is ___.

I hope (write what you hope about yourself and this person) ___.

201

Together, the topics provide students with writing that permits them to express their opinions and desires and to report on relevant personal experiences. This type of practice tends to provide good preparation for the kind of topically oriented writing assignments presented by many state writing assessments.

Writing Directions for Making Figures

Starting in lesson 45, students write directions for making figures such as:

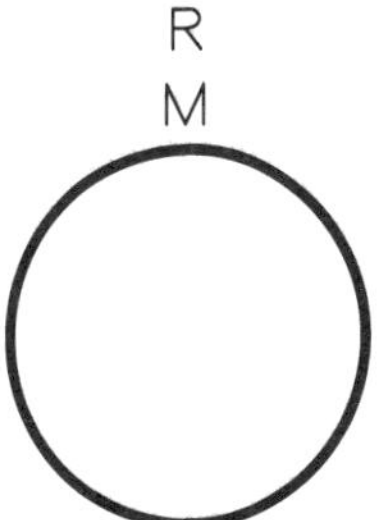

Students learn that the main part of the figure is the largest or most prominent part. They write about making that part first. Then they write about the additional details. Students must indicate what the additional details are and how the details are related to the main part or to another detail. In all, their descriptions must provide enough information for somebody to make a replica of the original figure.

Here's the exercise from extension lesson 46.

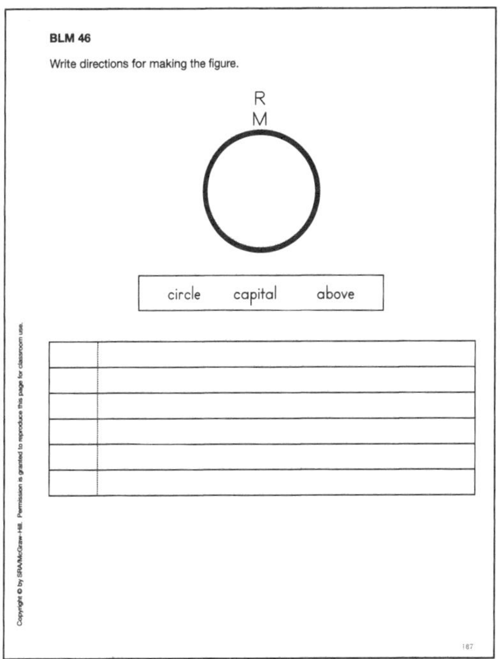

BLM 46

Write directions for making the figure.

R
M

circle capital above

187

1. (Hand out BLM 46.)
- You're going to write directions for making a figure.

2. You're going to write directions so that somebody would be able to make this figure. The parts of this figure are an **R,** an **M** and a circle.
- What's the main part of the figure? (Signal.) *A circle.*
- What's just above the circle? (Signal.) *M.*
- What's just above the **M**? (Signal.) *R.*

3. Write your sentence for making the main part of the figure. Raise your hand when you're finished.
(Observe students and give feedback.)
- Read your sentence. (Call on a student. Idea: *Make a large circle.*)

4. You're going to write sentences that tell about making the **R** and the **M.** First you write about the letter that is closest to the main part.
- Which letter are you going to write about first? (Signal.) *M.*
Yes, the **M.**
- Write your sentences for the **M** and for the **R.** Raise your hand when you're finished.
(Observe students and give feedback.)
- Read both your sentences. (Call on different students. Ideas: *Make an M just above the circle. Make an R just above the M.*)

5. Read your directions for making the whole figure. (Call on different students to read their directions. Tell how to rewrite parts that are not clear or are incorrect.)
6. Fix up your sentences so that you have written good directions for making the figure. Raise your hand when you're finished.
(Observe students and give feedback.)
7. Remember how you wrote your directions. First you told about the main part. Then you told about the part that is closest to the main part.

Poems

This activity begins in extension lesson 86. This activity is a team activity, with four students working together in each team. Students convert pairs of sentences that don't rhyme into pairs that do rhyme. Here's an example from lesson 86.

BLM 86

Make a poem from this story.

STORY	POEM
There once was a king. Ring was his name.	• There once was a king. ______
He always carried so much gold that he looked elderly.	• He always carried so much gold. ______
The gold was so heavy he couldn't walk or stand up tall. Sometimes, he would have to crawl around.	• He couldn't stand up tall. ______
He was a terrible sight. He called in a doctor late one evening.	• He was a terrible sight. ______ ______
The doctor said his problem was he was carrying too much gold with him. So he weighed a lot, even though he was a slim man.	• The doctor said the king had too much gold on him. ______ ______
So the king left his gold at home after that night. And from then on, he could stand up the right way.	• The king left his gold at home after that night. ______ ______
Now his face is full of smiles. He can walk a long, long way.	• Now his face is full of smiles. ______

208

1. (Hand out BLM 86 to each team.)
- I'm going to read you a story. You're going to make up a poem from the story I tell you. This is a hard assignment. You'll have to think and do a lot of rewriting before you get your poem the way you want it.

2. I'll read the story. The poem you'll write will be a funny poem about a king.

Here's a story about the king. Follow along:

> There once was a king. Ring was his name.
>
> He always carried so much gold that he looked elderly.
>
> The gold was so heavy he couldn't walk or stand up tall. Sometimes, he would have to crawl around.
>
> He was a terrible sight. He called in a doctor late one evening.
>
> The doctor said his problem was he was carrying too much gold with him. So he weighed a lot, even though he was a slim man.
>
> So the king left his gold at home after that night. And from then on, he could stand up the right way.
>
> Now his face is full of smiles. He can walk a long, long way.

3. The story doesn't have parts that rhyme, but some of the words are underlined. That means, you could use them as the last word in a line of the poem. The first part of what I read tells about the king's name and about his problem. What's the king's name? (Signal.) *Ring.*
- What's his problem? (Call on several students. Ideas: *He carried so much gold, he looked old. He couldn't do things.*)
- What were some of the things he couldn't do? (Call on several students. Ideas: *He couldn't stand up tall. He couldn't walk.*)
4. Listen. Start with this line: **There once was a king** and make up a line that rhymes. (Call on a student. Idea: *There once was a king. His name was [King]* ***Ring.***)
5. Listen. **He always carried so much gold, that he looked elderly.** Start with **he always carried so much gold,** and make up another ending that rhymes. (Call on a student. Idea: *He always carried so much gold,* ***that he looked [like he was very] old.***)
6. Your group is to make up lines that rhyme for the whole story. Remember, after you write two lines that rhyme with each other, you write two more lines that rhyme with each other. The last two lines do not have to rhyme with the first two lines. When you get lines that you like, somebody in the group should write them down. Raise your hand when your group is finished writing the poem.
7. (Observe and give feedback to groups as they work. If groups get stuck on parts of the poem, prompt them about how to create a pair of lines that rhyme.)

Key:
There once was a king.
His name was ***Ring.***

He always carried so much gold,
That he looked [very] ***old.***

The gold was so heavy he couldn't stand up tall.
Sometimes he would [fall and] ***crawl.***

He was a terrible sight.
He called a doctor late one ***night.***

The doctor said the king had too much gold on him.
He weighed a lot even though he was ***slim.***

The king left his gold at home after that night.
From then on he could stand up ***right.***

Now his face is full of smiles.
He can walk for ***miles and miles.***

Note: Other rhymes are possible. Not all groups should make up the same poem.

- (Do not require the same measure for each pair of lines that rhyme. As long as the measure is the same for both lines within a pair, the poem is acceptable.)

8. Check to make sure your poem tells the whole story. Each member of your group is to copy the group's poem. Raise your hand when you're finished. (Observe students and give feedback.)
9. (Have each group read its poem to the entire class.)
   - (You may require each group to memorize the group's poem and recite it to the class.)

Note that more than one rhyming pattern is possible for some of the sentence pairs.

Extension Lessons

Table of Contents

Before presenting Extension Lesson 1, see Scheduling the Extension Activities, page 4.

Extension Lesson 1

Materials: Each student will need a copy of BLM 1 and lined paper.

Objective: **Write parallel sentences that compare two similar pictures.**

REPORTING

COMPARING TWO PICTURES

BLM 1

corner licking floor boy's hand sitting

1.

2.

Write sentences that tell about the cat.

In picture 1, the cat is

Write sentences that tell about the glass.

In picture 1, the glass is

144

Copyright © by SRA/McGraw-Hill. Permission is granted to reproduce this page for classroom use.

1. (Hand out BLM 1.)
- You're going to compare these pictures. What are you going to do? (Signal.) *Compare these pictures.*

2. When you compare, you tell what is different about them.
- Touch the table in picture 1 and in picture 2. Keep touching both tables. ✔
  Listen: Is the table the same or different in the pictures? (Signal.) *Same.*
- Touch the chair in picture 1 and picture 2. ✔
  Listen: Is the chair the same or different in the pictures? (Signal.) *Same.*
- Touch the boy in both pictures. ✔
  Listen: Is the boy the same or different in the pictures? (Signal.) *Different.*

3. When you tell me what's different about the boy in the two pictures, you tell me what the boy is doing in the first picture and what the boy is doing in the second picture.
- Tell me about the boy in the first picture. (Call on a student. Idea: *The boy is holding a glass of milk.*)
- Tell me about the boy in the second picture. (Call on a student. Idea: *The boy is getting paper towels.*)

4. Touch the glass in both pictures. ✔
   Listen: Is the glass the same or different in the pictures? (Signal.) *Different.*
   When you tell me what's different about the glass in the two pictures, you tell me about the glass in the first picture and the glass in the second picture.
- Tell me about the glass in the first picture. (Call on a student. Idea: *The glass is in the boy's hand.*)
- Tell me about the glass in the second picture. (Call on a student. Idea: *The glass is on the floor.*)

5. Tell me about the floor in the first picture. (Call on different students. Ideas: *The floor is clean. It doesn't have milk on it.*)
- Tell me about the floor in the second picture. (Call on different students. Ideas: *It has milk and the glass on it. The floor is messy.*)

6. You're going to write sentences that compare some of the things that are different. For each thing you compare, you'll write one sentence that tells about the first picture and another sentence that tells about the second picture. You start both sentences with the words **in picture 1** or the words **in picture 2.**
- Look at the cat in both pictures. Here's a sentence you could write for picture 1: In picture 1, the cat is sitting in the corner of the room. Say that sentence. (Signal.) *In picture 1, the cat is sitting in the corner of the room.*
- In picture 2, the cat is licking milk from the floor. Say that sentence. (Signal.) *In picture 2, the cat is licking milk from the floor.*

7. The vocabulary box shows words that you could use in your sentences.

corner licking floor boy's hand sitting

- Your turn. Use lined paper. Write both sentences that tell about the cat in picture 1 and picture 2. Remember, one sentence for picture 1 and another sentence for picture 2. Start both sentences with the words **in picture.** Pencils down when you're finished. (Observe students and give feedback.)
- (Call on different students to read both sentences about the cat. Praise sentences that are correct. Ideas: *In picture 1, the cat is in the corner. In picture 1, the cat is sitting in the corner of the room. In picture 2, the cat is near the table. In picture 2, the cat is licking up the milk.*)

8. Everybody, touch the glass in both pictures. ✔
You're going to write about the glass in picture 1 and in picture 2. Write your sentence for picture 1. Remember to start with the words **in picture 1.** Pencils down when you're finished. (Observe students and give feedback.)
- (Call on different students to read their sentence for picture 1. Ideas: *In picture 1, the glass is in the boy's hand. In picture 1, the glass is filled with milk.*)

9. Everybody, write your sentence for the glass in picture 2. Pencils down when you're finished.
(Observe students and give feedback.)
- (Call on different students to read their sentence. Ideas: *In picture 2, the glass is on the floor. In picture 2, the glass doesn't have milk in it.*)

Extension Lesson 2

Materials: Each student will need a copy of BLM 2 and lined paper.

Objective: Write parallel sentences that compare two similar pictures.

REPORTING

COMPARING TWO PICTURES

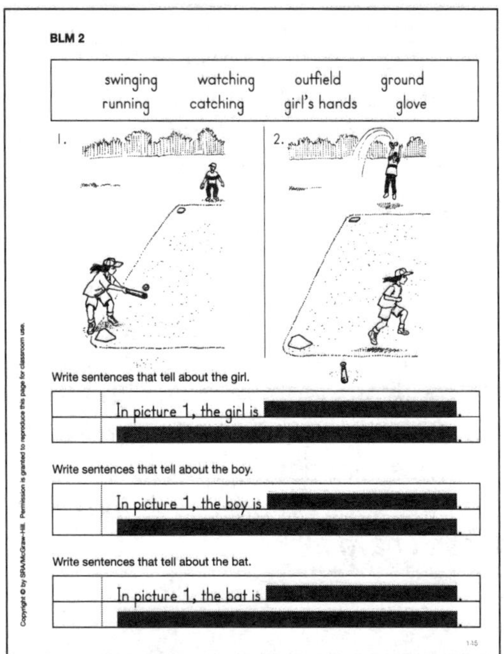

BLM 2

swinging	watching	outfield	ground
running	catching	girl's hands	glove

1. 2.

Write sentences that tell about the girl.

In picture 1, the girl is ______.

Write sentences that tell about the boy.

In picture 1, the boy is ______.

Write sentences that tell about the bat.

In picture 1, the bat is ______.

1. (Hand out BLM 2.)
- These pictures show what happened first and what happened next. You're going to compare these pictures. What are you going to do? (Signal.) *Compare these pictures.*

2. Touch the girl in picture 1 and in picture 2. Keep touching both pictures of the girl. ✔
   Listen: Is the girl the same or different in the pictures? (Signal.) *Different.*
- You're going to write about the girl in picture 1 and in picture 2. Use lined paper. The vocabulary box shows words you could use in your sentences.

swinging	watching	
outfield	ground	running
catching	girl's hands	glove

3. Start with the words **in picture 1** and write your sentence about the girl in picture 1. Pencils down when you're finished.
   (Observe students and give feedback.)
- Read your sentence. (Call on different students. Ideas: *In picture 1, the girl is swinging a bat. In picture 1, the girl is swinging the bat at the ball.*)
   (Do not accept sentences that refer to **she** instead of **the girl:** *In picture 1, **she** is swinging the bat at the ball.*)
   (Do not accept sentences that do not name **the girl:** *In picture 1, the bat is swinging.*)

4. Write your sentence for the girl in picture 2. Pencils down when you're finished.
   (Observe students and give feedback.)
- Read your sentence. (Call on a student. Idea: *In picture 2, the girl is running to first base.*)

5. Touch the boy in both pictures. ✔
   You're going to tell about the boy in both pictures.
- Write your sentence for the boy in picture 1. Pencils down when you're finished.
   (Observe students and give feedback.)

- Read your sentence. (Call on different students. Ideas: *In picture 1, the boy is watching the girl. In picture 1, the boy is standing and watching. In picture 1, the boy is standing in the outfield.*)

6. Write your sentence for the boy in picture 2. Pencils down when you're finished.
   (Observe students and give feedback.)

- Read your sentence. (Call on a student. Idea: *In picture 2, the boy is getting ready to catch the ball.*)

7. Touch the bat in both pictures. ✔
   You're going to tell about the bat in both pictures.

- Write your sentence for the bat in picture 1. Tell what the bat is doing in picture 1 or tell who is swinging the bat. Pencils down when you're finished.
  (Observe students and give feedback.)
- Read your sentence. (Call on different students. Ideas: *In picture 1, the bat is in the girl's hands. In picture 1, the girl is swinging the bat.*)

8. Write your sentence for the bat in picture 2. Pencils down when you're finished.
   (Observe students and give feedback.)

- Read your sentence. (Call on a student. Idea: *In picture 2, the bat is on the ground.*)

Extension Lesson 3

Materials: Each student will need a copy of BLM 3 and lined paper.

Objective: Write parallel sentences that compare two similar pictures.

REPORTING

COMPARING TWO PICTURES

BLM 3

reaching eat handing walking away
peel ground

1.
2.

Write sentences that tell about the monkey.

In picture 1, the monkey is

Write sentences that tell about the zookeeper.

In picture 1, the zookeeper is

Write sentences that tell about the banana.

In picture 1, the banana

146

1. (Hand out BLM 3.)
- You're going to compare these pictures. What are you going to do? (Signal.) *Compare these pictures.*
- What do you do when you compare pictures? (Call on a student. Idea: *Tell what's different about them.*)

2. Touch the monkey in both pictures. ✔ You're going to tell about the monkey in both pictures. Use lined paper.
- Write your sentence for the monkey in picture 1. Pencils down when you're finished. (Observe students and give feedback.)
- Read your sentence. (Call on different students. Ideas: *In picture 1, the monkey is reaching for a banana. In picture 1, the monkey is getting ready to grab the banana.*)
- Write your sentence for the monkey in picture 2. Pencils down when you're finished. (Observe students and give feedback.)
- Read your sentence. (Call on a student. Idea: *In picture 2, the monkey is eating the banana.*)

3. Touch the zookeeper in both pictures. ✔ You're going to tell about the zookeeper in both pictures.
- Write your sentence for the zookeeper in picture 1. Pencils down when you're finished. (Observe students and give feedback.)
- Read your sentence. (Call on a student. Idea: *In picture 1, the zookeeper is handing a banana to the monkey.*)
- Write your sentence for the zookeeper in picture 2. Pencils down when you're finished. (Observe students and give feedback.)
- Read your sentence. (Call on a student. Idea: *In picture 2, the zookeeper is walking away.*)

4. Touch the banana in both pictures. ✔ You're going to tell about the banana in both pictures.
- Write your sentence for the banana in picture 1. Tell how the banana looks or tell about the banana peel. Pencils down when you're finished. (Observe students and give feedback.)

- Read your sentence. (Call on different students. Ideas: *In picture 1, the banana peel is on the banana. In picture 1, the banana has a banana peel on it.*)
- Write your sentence for the banana in picture 2. Pencils down when you're finished.
  (Observe students and give feedback.)
- Read your sentence. (Call on different students. Ideas: *In picture 2, the banana peel is on the ground. In picture 2, the banana is peeled and part of it is missing.*)

Extension Lesson 4

Materials: Each student will need a copy of BLM 4 and lined paper.

Objective: Write parallel sentences that compare two similar pictures.

REPORTING

COMPARING TWO PICTURES

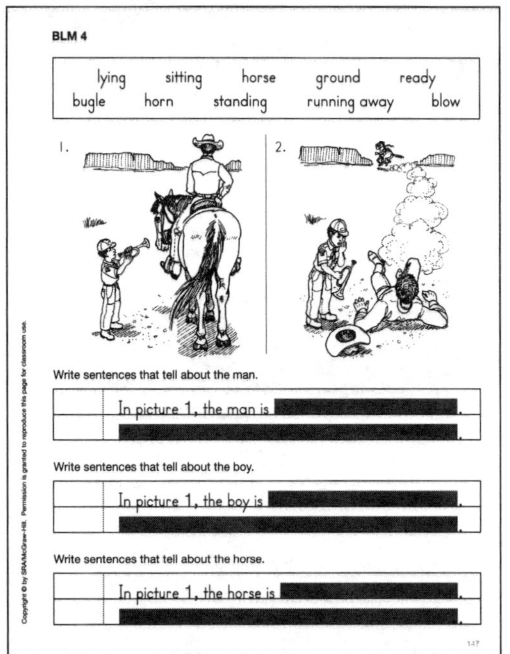

BLM 4

lying sitting horse ground ready
bugle horn standing running away blow

Write sentences that tell about the man.

In picture 1, the man is ▬▬▬▬.

Write sentences that tell about the boy.

In picture 1, the boy is ▬▬▬▬.

Write sentences that tell about the horse.

In picture 1, the horse is ▬▬▬▬.

1. (Hand out BLM 4.)
- These pictures show what happened first and what happened next. You're going to compare these pictures. What do you do when you compare pictures? (Call on a student. Idea: *Tell what's different about them.*)

2. Touch the man in both pictures. ✔ You're going to tell about the man in both pictures. Use lined paper.
- Write your sentence for the man in picture 1. Pencils down when you're finished. (Observe students and give feedback.)
- Read your sentence. (Call on different students. Ideas: *In picture 1, the man is sitting on his horse. In picture 1, the man is on the horse.*)
- Write your sentence for the man in picture 2. Pencils down when you're finished. (Observe students and give feedback.)
- Read your sentence. (Call on different students. Ideas: *In picture 2, the man is on the ground. In picture 2, the man is lying on the ground.*)

3. Touch the boy in both pictures. ✔ You're going to tell about the boy in both pictures.
- Write your sentence for the boy in picture 1. Pencils down when you're finished. (Observe students and give feedback.)
- Read your sentence. (Call on different students. Ideas: *In picture 1, the boy has his bugle by his mouth. In picture 1, the boy is getting ready to blow the horn.*)
- Write your sentence for the boy in picture 2. Pencils down when you're finished. (Observe students and give feedback.)
- Read your sentence. (Call on different students. Ideas: *In picture 2, the boy is holding his horn by his side. In picture 2, the boy is looking at the man on the ground.*)

4. Touch the horse in both pictures. ✔ You're going to tell about the horse in both pictures.

- Write your sentence for the horse in picture 1. Tell what the horse is doing. Pencils down when you're finished.
(Observe students and give feedback.)
- Read your sentence. (Call on different students. Ideas: *In picture 1, the horse is standing. In picture 1, the horse has a man on its back. In picture 1, the horse is looking at the horn*.)
- Write your sentence for the horse in picture 2. Pencils down when you're finished.
(Observe students and give feedback.)
- Read your sentence. (Call on different students. Ideas: *In picture 2, the horse is running away. In picture 2, the horse has no one on its back.*)

Extension Lesson 5

Materials: Each student will need a copy of BLM 5 and lined paper.

Objective: Write parallel sentences that compare two similar pictures.

REPORTING

COMPARING TWO PICTURES

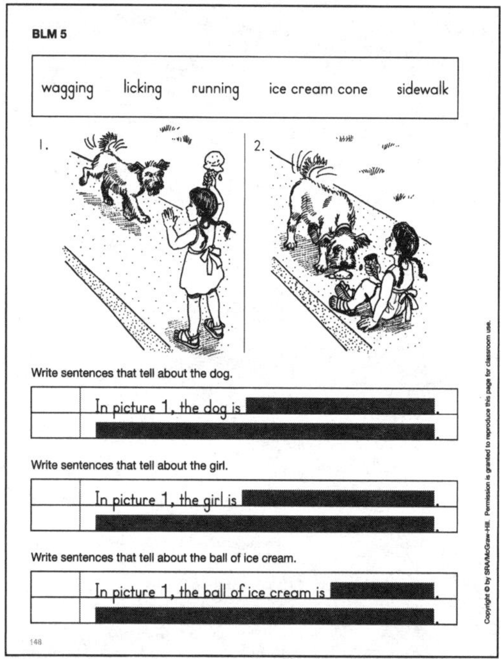

BLM 5

wagging licking running ice cream cone sidewalk

1. 2.

Write sentences that tell about the dog.

In picture 1, the dog is ______.

Write sentences that tell about the girl.

In picture 1, the girl is ______.

Write sentences that tell about the ball of ice cream.

In picture 1, the ball of ice cream is ______.

146

1. (Hand out BLM 5.)
- You're going to compare these pictures.

2. Touch the dog in both pictures. ✔
You're going to tell about the dog in both pictures. Use lined paper.
- Write your sentence for the dog in picture 1. Pencils down when you're finished.
(Observe students and give feedback.)
- Read your sentence. (Call on a student. Idea: *In picture 1, the dog is running toward the girl.*)
- Write your sentence for the dog in picture 2. Pencils down when you're finished.
(Observe students and give feedback.)
- Read your sentence. (Call on different students. Ideas: *In picture 2, the dog is eating the ice cream. In picture 2, the dog is next to the girl and licking the ice cream.*)

3. Touch the girl in both pictures. ✔
You're going to tell about the girl.
- Write your sentence for the girl in picture 1. Pencils down when you're finished.
(Observe students and give feedback.)
- Read your sentence. (Call on different students. Ideas: *In picture 1, the girl is holding her ice cream cone over her head. In picture 1, the girl is trying to keep her ice cream cone away from the dog.*)
- Write your sentence for the girl in picture 2. Pencils down when you're finished.
(Observe students and give feedback.)
- Read your sentence. (Call on different students. Ideas: *In picture 2, the girl is not holding an ice cream cone. In picture 2, the girl is sitting down and crying.*)

4. Touch the ball of ice cream in both pictures. ✔
You're going to tell about the ball of ice cream.
- Write your sentence for the ball of ice cream in picture 1. Tell where it is. Pencils down when you're finished.
(Observe students and give feedback.)

- Read your sentence. (Call on a student. Idea: *In picture 1, the ball of ice cream is in the cone.*)
- Write your sentence for the ball of ice cream in picture 2. Pencils down when you're finished.
  (Observe students and give feedback.)
- Read your sentence. (Call on a student. Idea: *In picture 2, the ball of ice cream is on the sidewalk.*)

Extension Lesson 6

Materials: Each student will need a copy of BLM 6 and lined paper.

Objective: **Write four or more sentences that infer what must have happened in a missing picture.**

INFERENCE
MISSING PICTURE

BLM 6

Write four or more sentences that tell about everything that must have happened in the middle picture. Remember, tell about **the boy, the glass, the milk** and **the cat.**

1. 2. 3.

floor boy's hand spilled dropped paper towels

1. (Hand out BLM 6.)
- You've told about pictures 1 and 3 before. This time, you're going to write about what happened in the middle picture. That's picture 2.

2. Touch something that is different in pictures 1 and 3. ✔
- Name something that is different in pictures 1 and 3. (Call on different students. Ideas: *Milk, boy, glass, floor, cat, paper towels.*)
- I'll name everything that's different in the pictures: the boy, the glass, the milk, the cat, the floor, the paper towels.
- Your turn. Name the things that are different. (Call on different students. Ideas: *The boy, the glass, the milk, the cat, the floor, the paper towels.*)

3. Listen: You're going to tell me about everything that happened to make picture 3 different. You have to tell me about **the boy, the glass, the milk** and **the cat.** What are you going to tell me about? (Signal.) *The boy, the glass, the milk and the cat.*
- Tell me what the boy must have done. (Call on a student. Ideas: *The boy dropped the glass. The boy went over to the paper towels.*)
- Tell me what happened to the glass. (Call on a student. Idea: *The glass fell on the floor.*)
- Tell me what happened to the milk. (Call on a student. Idea: *The milk spilled on the floor.*)
- Tell me what the cat did. (Call on a student. Idea: *The cat went over to the spilled milk.*)

4. Who can tell me everything that happened? (Call on different students. Praise accounts that tell about the boy, the glass, the milk and the cat.)

5. Your turn. Use lined paper. Write four or more sentences that tell about everything that must have happened in the middle picture. Remember, tell about the boy, the glass, the milk and the cat. Pencils down when you're finished.
   (Observe students and give feedback.)

- (Call on different students to read their accounts. Praise parts that are good. Offer suggestions for parts that are not clear or that are missing.)

Extension Lesson 7

Materials: Each student will need a copy of BLM 7 and lined paper.

Objective: Write four or more sentences that infer what must have happened in a missing picture.

INFERENCE

MISSING PICTURE

BLM 7

Write four or more sentences that tell about everything that must have happened in the middle picture. Remember, tell about **the girl, the bat, the ball** and **the boy.**

1.

2.

3.

toward dropped first base glove

1. (Hand out BLM 7.)
- You've told me about pictures 1 and 3 before. This time, you're going to write about what happened in the middle picture.
2. Touch something that is different in pictures 1 and 3. ✔
- Name something that is different in pictures 1 and 3. (Call on different students. Ideas: *Girl, ball, boy, bat.*)
- I'll name everything that's different in the pictures: the girl, the bat, the ball, the boy.
- Your turn. Name the things that are different. (Call on different students. Ideas: *The girl, the bat, the ball, the boy.*)
3. Listen: You're going to tell me about everything that happened to make picture 3 different. You have to tell me about **the girl, the bat, the ball** and **the boy.** What are you going to tell me about? (Signal.) *The girl, the bat, the ball and the boy.*
- Tell me why the ball is in a different place. (Call on a student. Idea: *The girl hit the ball with the bat.*)
- Tell me what the girl must have done with the bat after she hit the ball in the air. (Call on a student. Idea: *The girl dropped the bat on the ground.*)
- Tell me what the girl must have done after she dropped the bat. (Call on a student. Idea: *She started toward first base.*)
- Tell me what the boy must have done. (Call on a student. Idea: *Held his glove up so that he could catch the ball.*)
4. Who can tell me everything that happened? (Call on different students. Praise accounts that tell about the girl hitting the ball, dropping the bat, and moving toward first base; the ball going through the air to the boy; the boy raising his glove to catch the ball.)

5. Your turn. Use lined paper. Write four or more sentences that tell about everything that must have happened in the middle picture. Remember, tell about the girl, the boy, the bat and the ball. Pencils down when you're finished. (Observe students and give feedback.)

- (Call on different students to read their accounts. Praise parts that are good. Offer suggestions for parts that are not clear or that are missing.)

Extension Lesson 8

Materials: Each student will need a copy of BLM 8 and lined paper.

Objective: Write four or more sentences that infer what must have happened in a missing picture.

INFERENCE

MISSING PICTURE

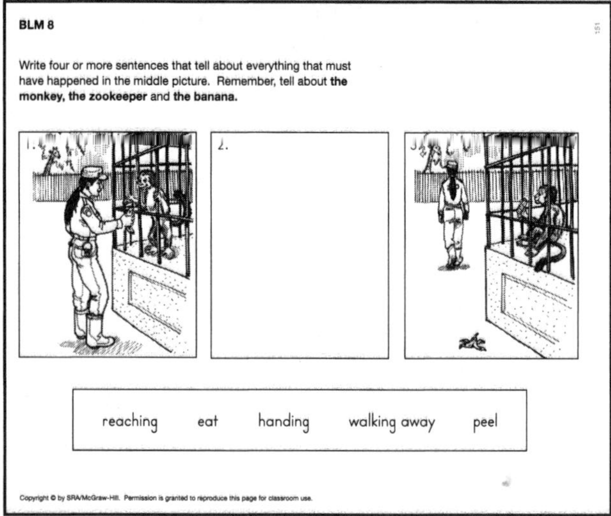

BLM 8

151

Write four or more sentences that tell about everything that must have happened in the middle picture. Remember, tell about **the monkey, the zookeeper** and **the banana.**

1. 2. 3.

reaching eat handing walking away peel

1. (Hand out BLM 8.)
- You've told me about pictures 1 and 3 before. This time, you're going to write about what happened in the middle picture.
2. Touch something that is different in pictures 1 and 3. ✔
- Name something that is different in pictures 1 and 3. (Call on different students. Ideas: *Monkey, banana, zookeeper.*)
3. Listen: You're going to tell me about everything that happened to make picture 3 different. You have to tell me about **the monkey, the zookeeper** and **the banana.** What are you going to tell me about? (Signal.) *The monkey, the zookeeper and the banana.*
- Tell me what the zookeeper must have done. (Call on a student. Idea: *Handed the banana to the monkey and walked away.*)
- Tell me everything the monkey did. (Call on a student. Idea: *Peeled the banana, sat down, ate part of the banana.*)
4. Who can tell me everything that happened? (Call on different students. Praise accounts that tell about the monkey, the zookeeper and the banana.)
5. Your turn. Use lined paper. Write four or more sentences that tell about everything that must have happened in the middle picture. Remember, tell about the monkey, the zookeeper and the banana. Pencils down when you're finished.
(Observe students and give feedback.)
- (Call on different students to read their accounts. Praise parts that are good. Offer suggestions for parts that are not clear or that are missing.)

Extension Lesson 9

Materials: Each student will need a copy of BLM 9 and lined paper.

Objective: Write four or more sentences that infer what must have happened in a missing picture.

INFERENCE

MISSING PICTURE

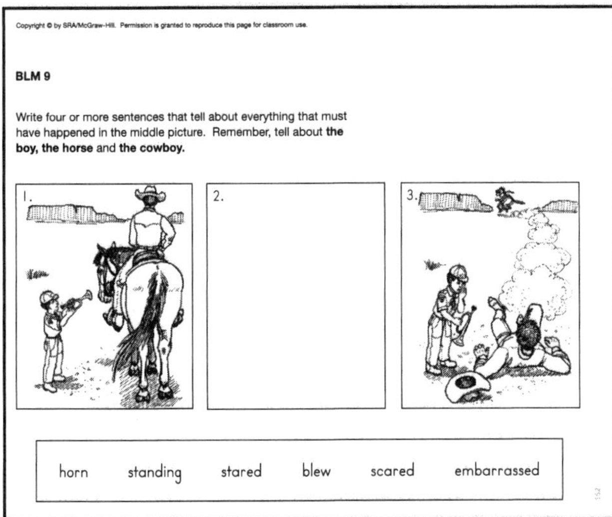

BLM 9

Write four or more sentences that tell about everything that must have happened in the middle picture. Remember, tell about **the boy, the horse** and **the cowboy.**

1. 2. 3.

horn standing stared blew scared embarrassed

1. (Hand out BLM 9.)
   - These pictures are supposed to show what happened first and next and next. I'll name everything that is different in pictures 1 and 3: the cowboy, the horse, the boy and his horn.
   - Your turn. Name the things that are different. (Call on a student. Idea: *The cowboy, the horse, the boy and his horn.*)
2. Listen: You're going to tell me about everything that happened to make picture 3 different. You have to start by telling about the boy and his horn. What do you start with? (Signal.) *The boy and his horn.*
   - Then tell about the horse and the cowboy. What will you tell about after the boy and his horn? (Signal.) *The horse and the cowboy.*
3. Who can tell me everything that happened? (Call on different students. Ideas: *The boy blew his horn. The horse got scared, bucked the cowboy off and ran away. The cowboy landed on the ground. The boy stared at him and felt embarrassed.*)
4. Your turn. Use lined paper. Write four or more sentences that tell about everything that must have happened in the middle picture. Remember, tell about the boy, the horse and the cowboy. Pencils down when you're finished.

   (Observe students and give feedback.)
   - (Call on different students to read their accounts. Praise parts that are good. Offer suggestions for parts that are not clear or that are missing.)

Extension Lesson 10

Materials: Each student will need a copy of BLM 10 and lined paper.

Objective: Write four or more sentences that infer what must have happened in a missing picture.

INFERENCE
MISSING PICTURE

BLM 10

153

Write four or more sentences that tell about everything that must have happened in the middle picture. Remember, tell about **the dog, the girl** and **the ice cream.**

licked ice cream sidewalk jumped

Copyright © by SRA/McGraw-Hill. Permission is granted to reproduce this page for classroom use.

1. (Hand out BLM 10.)
- You've told me about pictures 1 and 3 before. This time, you're going to write about what happened in the middle picture.
2. Touch something that is different in pictures 1 and 3. ✔
- Name something that is different in pictures 1 and 3. (Call on different students. Ideas: *Ice cream, girl, dog.*)
3. Listen: You're going to tell me about everything that happened to make picture 3 different. You have to start by telling about the dog and what it wanted to do. What do you start by telling about? (Call on a student. Idea: *The dog and what it wanted to do.*)
- Then tell about the girl and what she did first. What do you tell about after the dog? (Call on a student. Idea: *The girl and what she did first.*)
- Then tell what happened to the ice cream and what the dog did.
4. Who can tell me everything that happened? (Call on different students. Ideas: *The dog ran at the girl to get the ice cream. He jumped up on the girl. She fell down on her seat. The ice cream popped out of the cone and landed on the sidewalk. The dog licked the ice cream.*)
5. Your turn. Use lined paper. Write four or more sentences that tell about everything that must have happened in the middle picture. Remember, tell about the dog, the girl and the ice cream. Pencils down when you're finished.
(Observe students and give feedback.)
- (Call on different students to read their accounts. Praise parts that are good. Offer suggestions for parts that are not clear or that are missing.)

Extension Lesson 11

Materials: Each student will need a copy of BLM 11.

Objective: Alphabetize words that start with different letters.

ALPHABETICAL ORDER

BLM 11

Use the words below to make an alphabetical list.

great
carrot
top
horse
right
visit
elephant
north
jail
million

1. ______
2. ______
3. ______
4. ______
5. ______
6. ______
7. ______
8. ______
9. ______
10. ______

154

1. You're going to learn about alphabetical order. When you put words in alphabetical order, you look at the first letter of each word. Words that begin with **A** come first. Words that begin with **B** come next. Everybody, what words come after words that begin with **C**? (Signal.) *Words that begin with D.*
- What words come after words that begin with **D**? (Signal.) *Words that begin with E.*
2. Listen. Raise your hand when you know what comes after words that begin with **J.** (Call on a student. Idea: *Words that begin with K.*)
- Everybody, what comes after words that begin with **J**? (Signal.) *Words that begin with K.*
3. Raise your hand when you know what comes after words that begin with **X.** (Call on a student. Idea: *Words that begin with Y.*)
- Everybody, what comes after words that begin with **X**? (Signal.) *Words that begin with Y.*
4. (Hand out BLM 11.)
- The words in the box are not in alphabetical order. You'll find the word that should be first in an alphabetical list. No words begin with **A.** So what will you look for next? (Signal.) *Words that begin with B.*
- And if there are no words that begin with **B,** what will you look for next? (Signal.) *Words that begin with C.*
5. Raise your hand when you know which word in the box would be first in an alphabetical list.
- Everybody, which comes first? (Signal.) *Carrot.*
6. Raise your hand when you know which word comes after **carrot** in the alphabetical list. (Pause.)
- Everybody, which word comes after **carrot?** (Signal.) *Elephant.*
- Yes, there are no words that begin with **D.** But **elephant** begins with **E.**
7. (Write on the board:)

1. carrot
2. elephant

- Here are the first two words in the list. Your turn. Copy the first two words in your alphabetical list. Cross out the words **carrot** and **elephant** in the box. That shows that the words are already in your list. Then write the rest of the words in alphabetical order. After you write each word, cross it out in your box. When you're done, all ten words in the box should be crossed out. Raise your hand when you're finished.
(Observe students and give feedback.)

8. (Write to show:)

1. carrot	**6. million**
2. elephant	**7. north**
3. great	**8. right**
4. horse	**9. top**
5. jail	**10. visit**

- Here's what you should have. Fix up any mistakes.
(Observe students and give feedback.)

Extension Lesson 12

Materials: Each student will need a copy of BLM 12.

Objective: Alphabetize words that start with different letters.

ALPHABETICAL ORDER

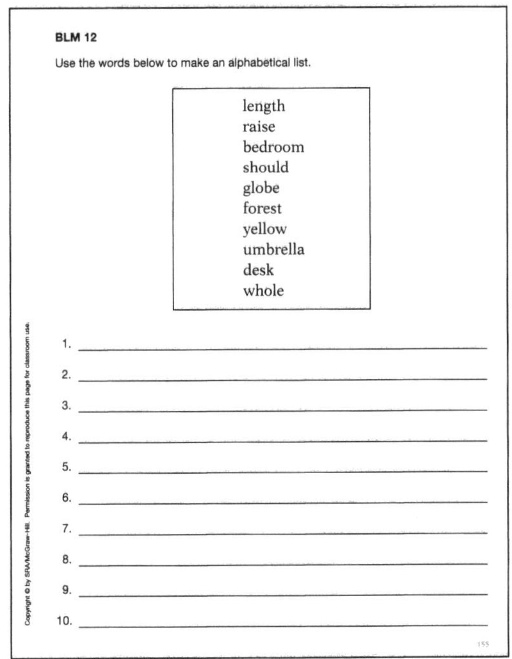

BLM 12

Use the words below to make an alphabetical list.

length
raise
bedroom
should
globe
forest
yellow
umbrella
desk
whole

1. ______
2. ______
3. ______
4. ______
5. ______
6. ______
7. ______
8. ______
9. ______
10. ______

Copyright © by SRA/McGraw-Hill. Permission is granted to reproduce this page for classroom use.

1. (Hand out BLM 12.)
   - You're going to put these ten words in alphabetical order. Figure out which word is the first in the list and write it. Then cross it out in your box. Raise your hand when you're finished. (Observe students and give feedback.)
2. (Write on the board:)

   1. bedroom

   - Here's what you should have for word 1: **bedroom.**
3. Complete the list. Remember to cross out each word when you write it in your list.
4. (Write to show:)

1. bedroom	**6. raise**
2. desk	**7. should**
3. forest	**8. umbrella**
4. globe	**9. whole**
5. length	**10. yellow**

   - Check your work. Here's the list you should have. Fix up any mistakes. (Observe students and give feedback.)

Extension Lesson 13

Materials: Each student will need a copy of BLM 13.

Objective: Alphabetize words that start with different letters.

ALPHABETICAL ORDER

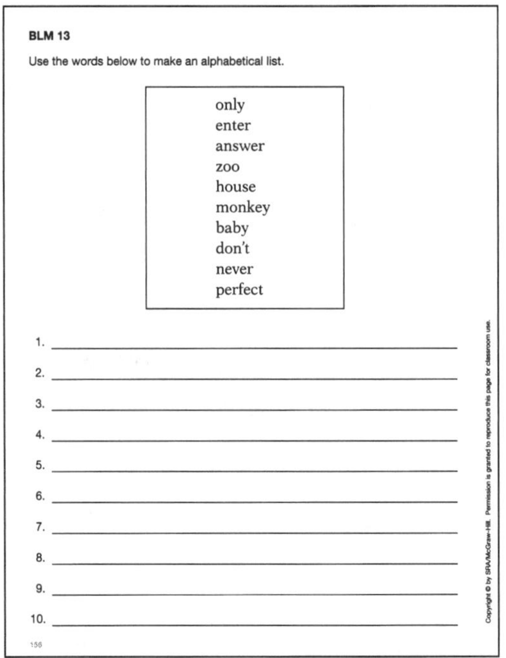

BLM 13

Use the words below to make an alphabetical list.

only
enter
answer
zoo
house
monkey
baby
don't
never
perfect

1. ______
2. ______
3. ______
4. ______
5. ______
6. ______
7. ______
8. ______
9. ______
10. ______

156

1. (Hand out BLM 13.)
- You're going to put these ten words in alphabetical order. Figure out which word is the first in the list and write it. Then cross it out in your box. Raise your hand when you're finished. (Observe students and give feedback.)

2. (Write on the board:)

1. answer

- Here's what you should have for word 1: **answer.**

3. Complete the list. Remember to cross out each word when you write it in your list.
4. (Write to show:)

1. answer	**6. monkey**
2. baby	**7. never**
3. don't	**8. only**
4. enter	**9. perfect**
5. house	**10. zoo**

- Check your work. Here's the list you should have. Fix up any mistakes. (Observe students and give feedback.)

Extension Lesson 14

Materials: Each student will need a copy of BLM 14.

Objective: Alphabetize words that start with different letters.

ALPHABETICAL ORDER

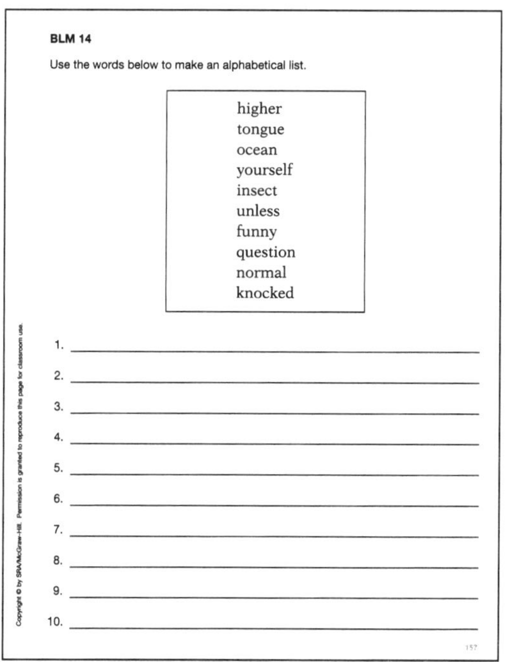

BLM 14

Use the words below to make an alphabetical list.

higher
tongue
ocean
yourself
insect
unless
funny
question
normal
knocked

1. ____
2. ____
3. ____
4. ____
5. ____
6. ____
7. ____
8. ____
9. ____
10. ____

1. (Hand out BLM 14.)
- You're going to put these ten words in alphabetical order. Figure out which word is the first in the list and write it. Then cross it out in your box. Raise your hand when you're finished. (Observe students and give feedback.)

2. (Write on the board:)

1. funny

- Here's what you should have for word 1: **funny.**

3. Complete the list. Remember to cross out each word when you write it in your list.
4. (Write to show:)

1. funny	**6. ocean**
2. higher	**7. question**
3. insect	**8. tongue**
4. knocked	**9. unless**
5. normal	**10. yourself**

- Check your work. Here's the list you should have. Fix up any mistakes. (Observe students and give feedback.)

Extension Lesson 15

Materials: Each student will need a copy of BLM 15.

Objective: Alphabetize words that start with different letters.

ALPHABETICAL ORDER

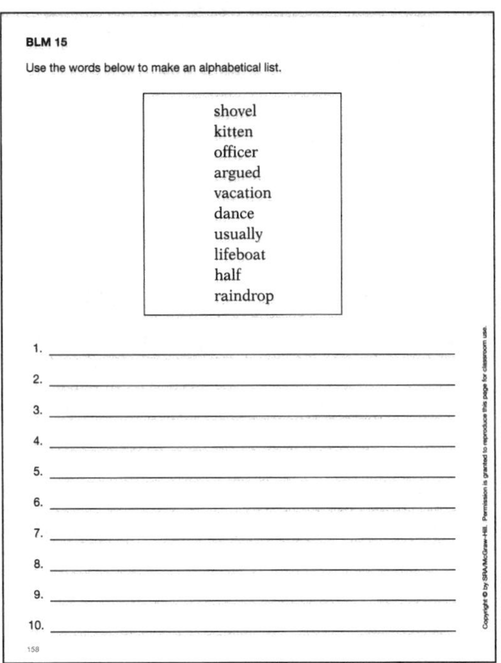

BLM 15

Use the words below to make an alphabetical list.

shovel
kitten
officer
argued
vacation
dance
usually
lifeboat
half
raindrop

1. ________
2. ________
3. ________
4. ________
5. ________
6. ________
7. ________
8. ________
9. ________
10. ________

158

1. (Hand out BLM 15.)
- You're going to put these ten words in alphabetical order. Figure out which word is the first in the list and write it. Then cross it out in your box. Raise your hand when you're finished. (Observe students and give feedback.)

2. (Write on the board:)

1. argued

- Here's what you should have for word 1: **argued.**

3. Complete the list. Remember to cross out each word when you write it in your list.
4. (Write to show:)

1. argued	**6. officer**
2. dance	**7. raindrop**
3. half	**8. shovel**
4. kitten	**9. usually**
5. lifeboat	**10. vacation**

- Check your work. Here's the list you should have. Fix up any mistakes. (Observe students and give feedback.)

Extension Lesson 16

Materials: Each student will need a copy of BLM 16.

Objective: Alphabetize words that start with different letters.

ALPHABETICAL ORDER

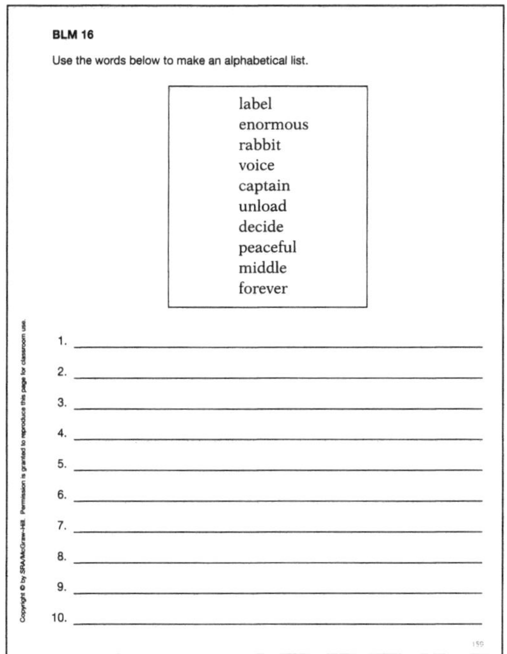

BLM 16

Use the words below to make an alphabetical list.

label
enormous
rabbit
voice
captain
unload
decide
peaceful
middle
forever

1. ______
2. ______
3. ______
4. ______
5. ______
6. ______
7. ______
8. ______
9. ______
10. ______

1. (Hand out BLM 16.)
- You're going to put these ten words in alphabetical order. Figure out which word is the first in the list and write it. Then cross it out in your box. Raise your hand when you're finished. (Observe students and give feedback.)

2. (Write on the board:)

1. captain

- Here's what you should have for word 1: **captain.**

3. Complete the list. Remember to cross out each word when you write it in your list.
4. (Write to show:)

1. captain	**6. middle**
2. decide	**7. peaceful**
3. enormous	**8. rabbit**
4. forever	**9. unload**
5. label	**10. voice**

- Check your work. Here's the list you should have. Fix up any mistakes. (Observe students and give feedback.)

Extension Lesson 17

Materials: Each student will need a copy of BLM 17.

Objective: Alphabetize words that start with different letters.

ALPHABETICAL ORDER

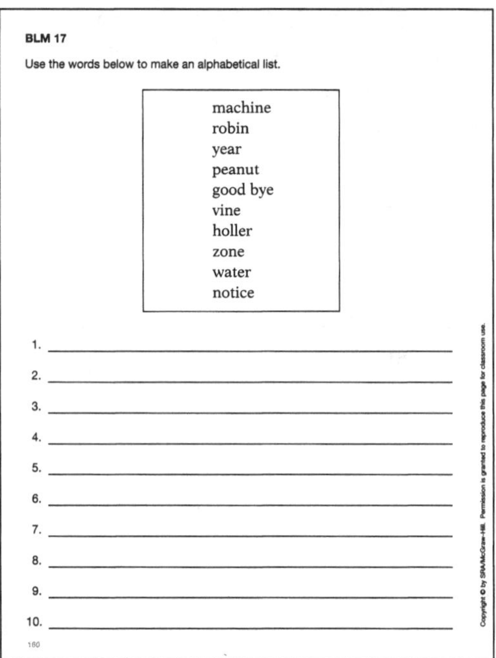

BLM 17

Use the words below to make an alphabetical list.

machine
robin
year
peanut
good bye
vine
holler
zone
water
notice

1. ____
2. ____
3. ____
4. ____
5. ____
6. ____
7. ____
8. ____
9. ____
10. ____

160

1. (Hand out BLM 17.)
   - You're going to put these ten words in alphabetical order. Figure out which word is the first in the list and write it. Then cross it out in your box. Raise your hand when you're finished.
   (Observe students and give feedback.)
2. (Write on the board:)

   1. good bye

   - Here's what you should have for word 1: **good bye.**
3. Complete the list. Remember to cross out each word when you write it in your list.
4. (Write to show:)

1. good bye	**6. robin**
2. holler	**7. vine**
3. machine	**8. water**
4. notice	**9. year**
5. peanut	**10. zone**

   - Check your work. Here's the list you should have. Fix up any mistakes.
   (Observe students and give feedback.)

Extension Lesson 18

Materials: Each student will need a copy of BLM 18.

Objective: **Alphabetize words that start with the same letter.**

ALPHABETICAL ORDER

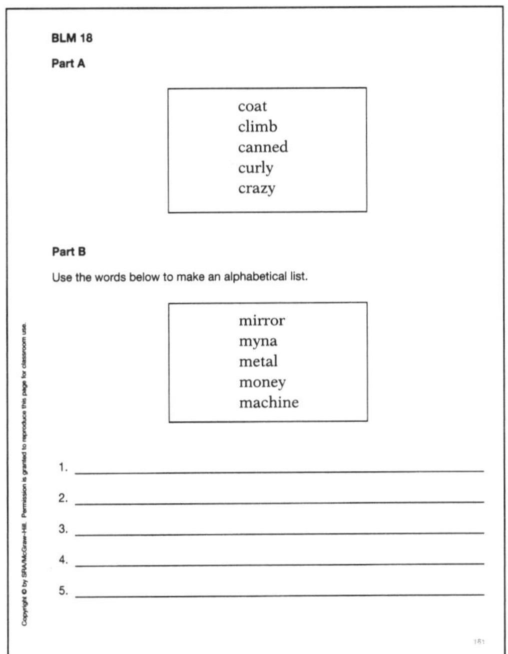

BLM 18

Part A

coat
climb
canned
curly
crazy

Part B

Use the words below to make an alphabetical list.

mirror
myna
metal
money
machine

1. ________
2. ________
3. ________
4. ________
5. ________

1. (Hand out BLM 18.)
- You've put lists of words in alphabetical order. For each list you've worked with, all the words started with different letters. Some lists have more than one word that starts with the same letter. What do you do then? You look at the **second** letter in each word.

2. All the words in part A begin with the letter **C.**
- (Teacher reference:)

coat
climb
canned
curly
crazy

- Look at the **second** letter of each word. Find the second letter that comes before the others in the alphabet. Raise your hand when you've found the second letter that comes earliest. (Wait.)
- Everybody, which second letter comes earliest? (Signal.) *A.*
- So the word **canned** would come first in an alphabetical list.
- (Write on the board:)

1. canned

3. Raise your hand when you know which second letter comes next in an alphabetical list. (Wait.)
- Everybody, which second letter comes next in the list? (Signal.) *L.*
- So the first two words are **canned** and **climb.**
- (Write to show:)

1. canned
2. climb

4. Raise your hand when you know which second letter comes after **L.** (Wait.)
- Everybody, which second letter comes after **L**? (Signal.) *O.*
- So **coat** is the third word in the list.
- (Write to show:)

2. climb
3. coat

5. Raise your hand when you know which second letter comes after **O.** (Wait.)
- Everybody, which second letter comes after **O**? (Signal.) *R.*
- So which word comes after **coat**? (Signal.) *Crazy.*
- (Write to show:)

3. coat
4. crazy

6. And which second letter comes after **R**? (Signal.) *U.*
- So which word is last in the list? (Signal.) *Curly.*
- (Write to show:)

4. crazy
5. curly

7. Find part B. ✔
- All the words in part B begin with the letter **M.** Underline the second letter in each word so you'll see the letters you are using. Then write the words in alphabetical order.
(Observe students and give feedback.)

8. (Write on the board:)

1. machine
2. metal
3. mirror
4. money
5. myna

- Check your work. Here's what you should have. Fix up any mistakes. ✔

Extension Lesson 19

Materials: Each student will need a copy of BLM 19.

Objective: Alphabetize words that start with the same letter.

ALPHABETICAL ORDER

BLM 19

Underline the second letter in each word. Then write the words in alphabetical order.

oven
once
officer
ocean
outfit

1. ______
2. ______
3. ______
4. ______
5. ______

192

1. (Hand out BLM 19.)
   - All the words in the box begin with the letter **O.** Underline the second letter in each word. Then write the words in alphabetical order.

   (Observe students and give feedback.)

2. (Write on the board:)

   1. ocean
   2. officer
   3. once
   4. outfit
   5. oven

   - Check your work. Here's what you should have. Fix up any mistakes. ✔

Materials: Each student will need a copy of BLM 20.

Objective: Alphabetize words that start with the same letter.

ALPHABETICAL ORDER

BLM 20

Underline the second letter in each word. Then write the words in alphabetical order.

swallow
squirrel
steady
scale
second
solid
smelly
shelves

1. ______
2. ______
3. ______
4. ______
5. ______
6. ______
7. ______
8. ______

163

1. (Hand out BLM 20.)

- All the words in the box begin with the letter **S.** Underline the second letter in each word. Then write the words in alphabetical order.
  (Observe students and give feedback.)

2. (Write on the board:)

1. scale
2. second
3. shelves
4. smelly
5. solid
6. squirrel
7. steady
8. swallow

- Check your work. Here's what you should have. Fix up any mistakes. ✔

Extension Lesson 21

Materials: Each student will need a copy of BLM 21.

Objective: Alphabetize words that start with the same letter.

ALPHABETICAL ORDER

BLM 21

Underline the second letter in each word. Then write the words in alphabetical order.

boast
building
blew
breath
beyond
billows

1. ______
2. ______
3. ______
4. ______
5. ______
6. ______

194

1. (Hand out BLM 21.)

- All the words in the box begin with the letter **B.** Underline the second letter in each word. Then write the words in alphabetical order.

  (Observe students and give feedback.)

2. (Write on the board:)

1. beyond
2. billows
3. blew
4. boast
5. breath
6. building

- Check your work. Here's what you should have. Fix up any mistakes. ✔

Extension Lesson 22

Materials: Each student will need a copy of BLM 22.

Objective: Alphabetize words that start with the same letter.

ALPHABETICAL ORDER

BLM 22

Underline the second letter in each word. Then write the words in alphabetical order.

eraser
enormous
edge
easy
evening
escape
eggs
eyes

1. ______
2. ______
3. ______
4. ______
5. ______
6. ______
7. ______
8. ______

165

1. (Hand out BLM 22.)

- All the words in the box begin with the letter **E.** Underline the second letter in each word. Then write the words in alphabetical order.
  (Observe students and give feedback.)

2. (Write on the board:)

1. easy
2. edge
3. eggs
4. enormous
5. eraser
6. escape
7. evening
8. eyes

- Check your work. Here's what you should have. Fix up any mistakes. ✔

Extension Lesson 23

Materials: Each student will need a copy of BLM 23.

Objective: **Alphabetize words (mixed set).**

ALPHABETICAL ORDER

BLM 23

change
cabbage
dollar
coast
decide
dream
circus

1. ______
2. ______
3. ______
4. ______
5. ______
6. ______
7. ______

190

1. (Hand out BLM 23.)
- The list of words in the box has words that begin with **C** and words that begin with **D.** Everybody, which comes first in the alphabet, words that begin with **C** or words that begin with **D**? (Signal.) *Words that begin with C.*
2. Circle each word that begins with **C.** Raise your hand when you've done that much.
(Observe students and give feedback.)
- The words you should have circled are **change, cabbage, coast** and **circus.** Fix up any mistakes. ✔
- You'll put all those circled words in your list before you put in any of the words that begin with **D.**
3. Listen: Underline the second letter of each word that begins with **C.** Those are the words you circled.
(Observe students and give feedback.)
4. Now write all the **C** words in alphabetical order. Remember to look at the second letter of each word. Raise your hand when you're finished.
(Observe students and give feedback.)
5. (Write on the board:)

1. cabbage
2. change
3. circus
4. coast

- Check your work. Here's what you should have so far. Fix up any mistakes. ✔
6. Now you're going to put all the words that begin with **D** in your list. Underline the second letter of each **D** word and write the **D** words in alphabetical order after the **C** words. Raise your hand when you're finished.
(Observe students and give feedback.)
7. (Write to show:)

4. coast
5. decide
6. dollar
7. dream

- Check your work. Here's what you should have. Raise your hand if you got everything right.

Extension Lesson 24

Materials: Each student will need a copy of BLM 24.

Objective: Alphabetize words (mixed set).

ALPHABETICAL ORDER

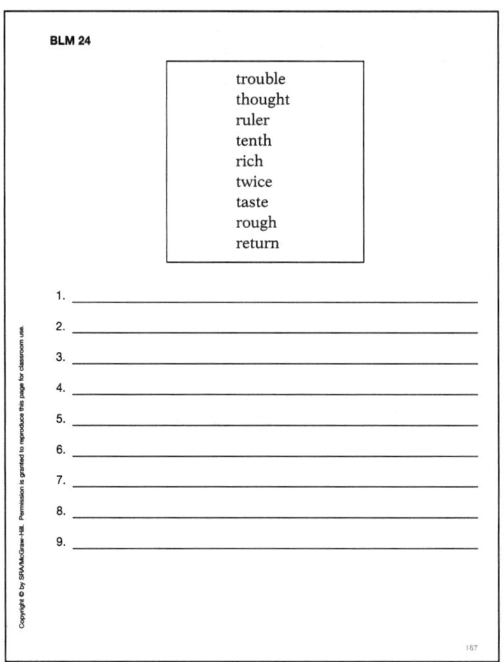

BLM 24

trouble
thought
ruler
tenth
rich
twice
taste
rough
return

1. __________
2. __________
3. __________
4. __________
5. __________
6. __________
7. __________
8. __________
9. __________

167

1. (Hand out BLM 24.)
- The list of words in the box has words that begin with **T** and words that begin with **R.** Everybody, which comes first in the alphabet, words that begin with **T** or words that begin with **R**? (Signal.) *Words that begin with R.*

2. Circle each word in the box that begins with **R.** Raise your hand when you've done that much.
(Observe students and give feedback.)
- The words you should have circled are **ruler, rich, rough** and **return.** Fix up any mistakes. ✔
- You'll put all those circled words in your list before you put in any of the words that begin with **T.**

3. Listen: Underline the second letter of each word that begins with **R.** Those are the words you circled.
(Observe students and give feedback.)

4. Now write all the **R** words in alphabetical order. Remember to look at the second letter of each word. Raise your hand when you're finished.
(Observe students and give feedback.)

5. (Write on the board:)

1. return
2. rich
3. rough
4. ruler

- Check your work. Here's what you should have so far. Fix up any mistakes. ✔

6. Now you're going to put all the words that begin with **T** in your list. Underline the second letter of each **T** word and write the **T** words in alphabetical order after the **R** words. Raise your hand when you're finished.
(Observe students and give feedback.)

7. (Write to show:)

4. ruler
5. taste
6. tenth
7. thought
8. trouble
9. twice

- Check your work. Here's what you should have. Raise your hand if you got everything right.

Extension Lesson 25

Materials: Each student will need a copy of BLM 25.

Objective: Alphabetize words (mixed set).

ALPHABETICAL ORDER

BLM 25

middle
island
machine
insist
mummy
money
idea

1. ________
2. ________
3. ________
4. ________
5. ________
6. ________
7. ________

1. (Hand out BLM 25.)
   - The list of words in the box has words that begin with **M** and words that begin with **I.** Everybody, which comes first in the alphabet, words that begin with **M** or words that begin with **I?** (Signal.) *Words that begin with I.*
2. Circle each word in the box that begins with **I.** Raise your hand when you've done that much.
   (Observe students and give feedback.)
   - Check your work. The words you should have circled are **island, insist** and **idea.** Fix up any mistakes. ✔
   - You'll put all those circled words in your list before you put in any of the words that begin with **M.**
3. Listen: Underline the second letter of each word that begins with **I.** Those are the words you circled.
   (Observe students and give feedback.)
4. Now write all the **I** words in alphabetical order. Remember to look at the second letter of each word. Raise your hand when you're finished.
   (Observe students and give feedback.)
5. (Write on the board:)

   1. idea
   2. insist
   3. island

   - Check your work. Here's what you should have so far. Fix up any mistakes. ✔
6. Now you're going to put all the words that begin with **M** in your list. Underline the second letter of each **M** word and write the **M** words in alphabetical order after the **I** words. Raise your hand when you're finished.
   (Observe students and give feedback.)
7. (Write to show:)

   3. island
   4. machine
   5. middle
   6. money
   7. mummy

   - Check your work. Here's what you should have. Raise your hand if you got everything right.

Extension Lesson 26

Materials: Each student will need a copy of BLM 26.

Objective: Alphabetize words (mixed set).

ALPHABETICAL ORDER

BLM 26

flower
juggle
football
fence
fifty
join

1. ______
2. ______
3. ______
4. ______
5. ______
6. ______

1. (Hand out BLM 26.)

- The list of words in the box has words that begin with **J** and words that begin with **F.** Everybody, which comes first in the alphabet, words that begin with **J** or words that begin with **F**? (Signal.) *Words that begin with F.*

2. Circle all the words that begin with **F** and put them in alphabetical order. Then put all the words that begin with **J** in your list. Put those words in alphabetical order.
(Observe students and give feedback.)
3. (Write on the board:)

1. fence
2. fifty
3. flower
4. football
5. join
6. juggle

- Check your work. Here's what you should have. Raise your hand if you got everything right.

Extension Lesson 27

Materials: Each student will need a copy of BLM 27.

Objective: Alphabetize words (mixed set).

ALPHABETICAL ORDER

BLM 27

thirsty
notice
twice
terrible
neither
traffic
toast

1. ______
2. ______
3. ______
4. ______
5. ______
6. ______
7. ______

170

1. (Hand out BLM 27.)
- The list of words in the box has words that begin with **N** and words that begin with **T.** Everybody, which comes first in the alphabet, words that begin with **N** or words that begin with **T**? (Signal.) *Words that begin with N.*

2. Circle all the words that begin with **N** and put them in alphabetical order. Then put all the words that begin with **T** in your list. Put those words in alphabetical order.
(Observe students and give feedback.)
3. (Write on the board:)

1. neither
2. notice
3. terrible
4. thirsty
5. toast
6. traffic
7. twice

- Check your work. Here's what you should have. Raise your hand if you got everything right.

Extension Lesson 28

Materials: Each student will need a copy of BLM 28.

Objective: Alphabetize words (mixed set).

ALPHABETICAL ORDER

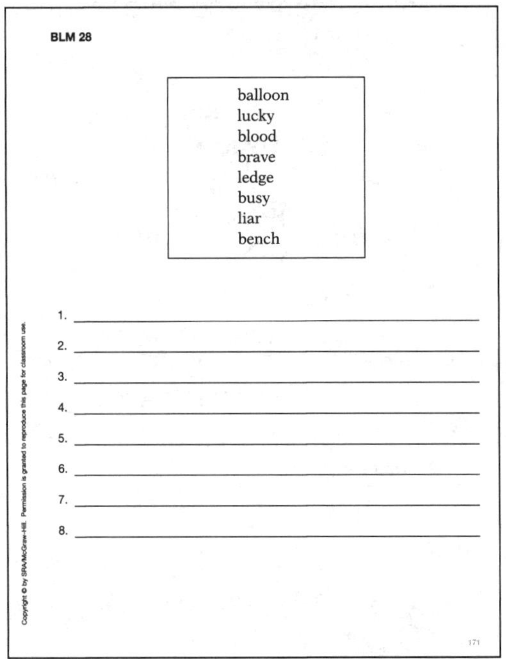

BLM 28

balloon
lucky
blood
brave
ledge
busy
liar
bench

1. ______
2. ______
3. ______
4. ______
5. ______
6. ______
7. ______
8. ______

171

1. (Hand out BLM 28.)
- The list of words in the box has words that begin with **L** and words that begin with **B.** Everybody, which comes first in the alphabet, words that begin with **L** or words that begin with **B**? (Signal.) *Words that begin with B.*

2. Circle all the words that begin with **B** and put them in alphabetical order. Then put all the words that begin with **L** in your list. Put those words in alphabetical order. (Observe students and give feedback.)
3. (Write on the board:)

1. balloon
2. bench
3. blood
4. brave
5. busy
6. ledge
7. liar
8. lucky

- Check your work. Here's what you should have. Raise your hand if you got everything right.

Extension Lesson 29

Materials: Each student will need a copy of BLM 29.

Objective: Alphabetize words (mixed set).

ALPHABETICAL ORDER

BLM 29

ruler
airplane
done
knives
thumb
dinner
ceiling
report
honest
weather

1. ____
2. ____
3. ____
4. ____
5. ____
6. ____
7. ____
8. ____
9. ____
10. ____

1. (Hand out BLM 29.)
   - Here's a list of words that you'll put in alphabetical order. Most of the words do not begin with the same letter, but two words begin with **D** and two words begin with **R.**
2. Write the words that come before **D.** Don't write **done** or **dinner,** but write all the words that come before **done** or **dinner.**
   (Observe students and give feedback.)
3. (Write on the board:)

   1. airplane
   2. ceiling

   - Check your work. Here are the words you should have so far. Fix up any mistakes.
4. Now put **done** and **dinner** in the list. Look at the second letter of each word to see which word comes first and which word comes next.
   (Observe students and give feedback.)
5. (Write to show:)

   2. ceiling
   3. dinner
   4. done

   - Check your work. Here's what you should have. Fix up any mistakes.
6. Now write the words that come after **D** but before **R.** Don't write the words that begin with **R.**
   (Observe students and give feedback.)
7. (Write to show:)

   4. done
   5. honest
   6. knives

   - Check your work. Here's what you should have. Fix up any mistakes.

8. Now put in the words that begin with **R.** Remember, look at the second letters. Then write the rest of the words in the list.
   (Observe students and give feedback.)
9. (Write to show:)

   6. knives
   7. report
   8. ruler
   9. thumb
   10. weather

- Check your work. Here's what you should have. Raise your hand if you got everything right.

Extension Lesson 30

Materials: Each student will need a copy of BLM 30.

Objective: Alphabetize words (mixed set).

ALPHABETICAL ORDER

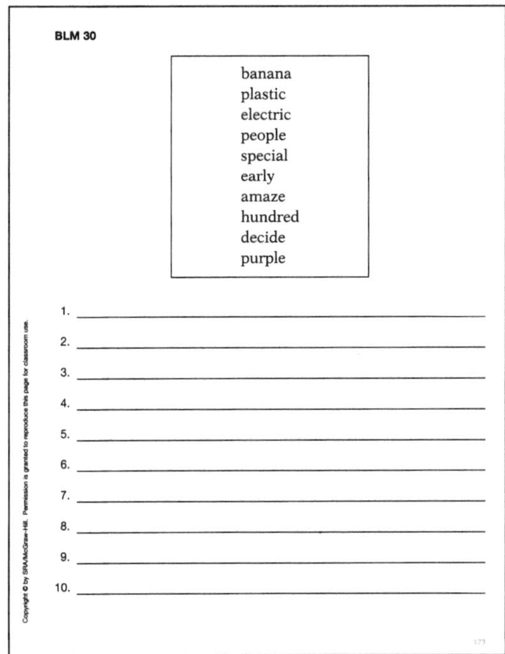

BLM 30

banana
plastic
electric
people
special
early
amaze
hundred
decide
purple

1. __________
2. __________
3. __________
4. __________
5. __________
6. __________
7. __________
8. __________
9. __________
10. __________

1. (Hand out BLM 30.)
- Here's a list of words that you'll put in alphabetical order. Most of the words do not begin with the same letter, but two words begin with **E** and three words begin with **P.**

2. Write the words that come before **E.** Don't write **electric** or **early,** but write all the words that come before **electric** or **early.**
(Observe students and give feedback.)

3. (Write on the board:)

1. amaze
2. banana
3. decide

- Check your work. Here are the words you should have so far. Fix up any mistakes.

4. Now put **electric** and **early** in the list. Look at the second letter of each word to see which word comes first and which word comes next.
(Observe students and give feedback.)

5. (Write to show:)

3. decide
4. early
5. electric

- Check your work. Here's what you should have. Fix up any mistakes.

6. Now write the words that come after **E** but before **P.** Don't write the words that begin with **P.**
(Observe students and give feedback.)

7. (Write to show:)

4. early
5. electric
6. hundred

- Check your work. Here's what you should have. Fix up any mistakes.

8. Now put in the words that begin with **P.** Remember, look at the second letters. Then write the rest of the words in the list.
   (Observe students and give feedback.)
9. (Write to show:)

   6. hundred
   7. people
   8. plastic
   9. purple
   10. special

- Check your work. Here's what you should have. Raise your hand if you got everything right.

Extension Lesson 31

Materials: Each student will need a copy of BLM 31.

Objective: Alphabetize words (mixed set).

ALPHABETICAL ORDER

BLM 31

shadow
lemon
giant
visit
destroy
great
younger
bread
space
globe

1. ________
2. ________
3. ________
4. ________
5. ________
6. ________
7. ________
8. ________
9. ________
10. ________

174

1. (Hand out BLM 31.)
- Here's a list of words that you'll put in alphabetical order. Most of the words do not begin with the same letter, but three words begin with **G** and two words begin with **S.**

2. Write the words that come before **G.** Don't write the **G** words, but write all the words that come before the **G** words.
(Observe students and give feedback.)

3. (Write on the board:)

1. bread
2. destroy

- Check your work. Here are the words you should have so far. Fix up any mistakes.

4. Now put the **G** words in the list. Look at the second letter of each word to see which word comes first.
(Observe students and give feedback.)

5. (Write to show:)

2. destroy
3. giant
4. globe
5. great

- Check your work. Here's what you should have. Fix up any mistakes.

6. Now write the words that come after **G** but before **S.** Don't write the words that begin with **S.**
(Observe students and give feedback.)

7. (Write to show:)

4. globe
5. great
6. lemon

- Check your work. Here's what you should have. Fix up any mistakes.

8. Now put in the words that begin with **S.** Remember, look at the second letters. Then write the rest of the words in the list.
   (Observe students and give feedback.)
9. (Write to show:)

   6. lemon
   7. shadow
   8. space
   9. visit
   10. younger

- Check your work. Here's what you should have. Raise your hand if you got everything right.

Extension Lesson 32

Materials: Each student will need a copy of BLM 32.

Objective: Alphabetize words (mixed set).

ALPHABETICAL ORDER

BLM 32

count
collar
complete
cob
cod
coat
cone
cook

1. __________
2. __________
3. __________
4. __________
5. __________
6. __________
7. __________
8. __________

175

1. (Hand out BLM 32.)
- In all the words in the box, the first two letters are the same. All the words begin with the letters **C-O.** To put these words in alphabetical order, you have to look at the **third** letter in the words.
2. Underline the third letter in each word. Raise your hand when you've done that much.
   (Observe students and give feedback.)
3. Raise your hand when you know which of these words comes first in the alphabet. (Wait.)
- Everybody, which word comes first? (Signal.) *Coat.*
- Yes, **C-O-A** comes before **C-O-B** or any of the other words that start with **C-O.**
4. Write all the words in alphabetical order. Raise your hand when you're finished. (Observe students and give feedback.)
5. (Write on the board:)

1. coat
2. cob
3. cod
4. collar
5. complete
6. cone
7. cook
8. count

- Check your work. Here's what you should have. Fix up any mistakes.

Materials: Each student will need a copy of BLM 33.

Objective: Alphabetize words (mixed set).

ALPHABETICAL ORDER

BLM 33

dry
driver
draft
dream
drop
drum

1. __________
2. __________
3. __________
4. __________
5. __________
6. __________

175

1. (Hand out BLM 33.)
   - All the words in the box begin with the same letters—**D-R.** So you have to look at the third letter of each word to figure out the alphabetical order.
2. Look at the third letter in each word. Then write the words in alphabetical order. Raise your hand when you're finished.
   (Observe students and give feedback.)
3. (Write on the board:)

   1. draft
   2. dream
   3. driver
   4. drop
   5. drum
   6. dry

   - Check your work. Here's what you should have. Fix up any mistakes.

Extension Lesson 34

Materials: Each student will need a copy of BLM 34.

Objective: **Alphabetize words between guide words.**

ALPHABETICAL ORDER

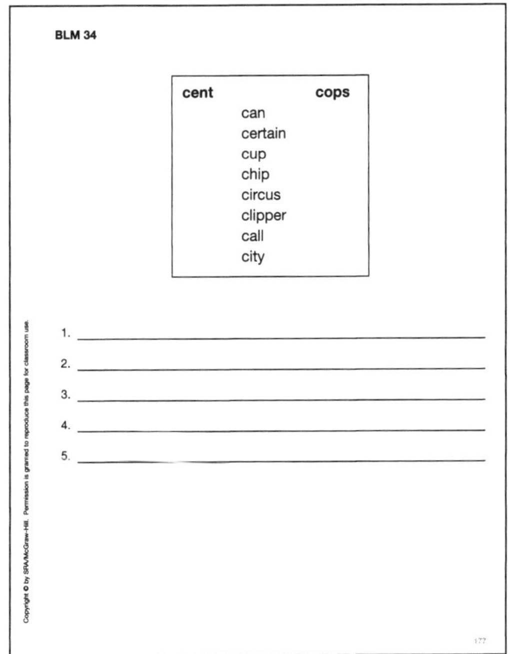

BLM 34

cent	cops
can	
certain	
cup	
chip	
circus	
clipper	
call	
city	

1. __________
2. __________
3. __________
4. __________
5. __________

177

1. (Hand out BLM 34.)
- The words at the top of the box are **cent** and **cops.** **Cent** comes first in the alphabet. **Cops** comes later in the alphabet.
- Five of the words below come between **cent** and **cops** in the alphabet. Those words come after **cent** but before **cops.**

2. Write the five words that are between **cent** and **cops.** Write them in alphabetical order. For some of the words, the first two letters are the same, so you'll have to look at the third letter to see which is earlier in the alphabet. Raise your hand when you're finished. (Observe students and give feedback.)
3. (Write on the board:)

> **1. certain**
> **2. chip**
> **3. circus**
> **4. city**
> **5. clipper**

- Check your work. Here's what you should have. Fix up any mistakes.

Extension Lesson 35

Materials: Each student will need a copy of BLM 35.
Objective: Alphabetize words between guide words.

ALPHABETICAL ORDER

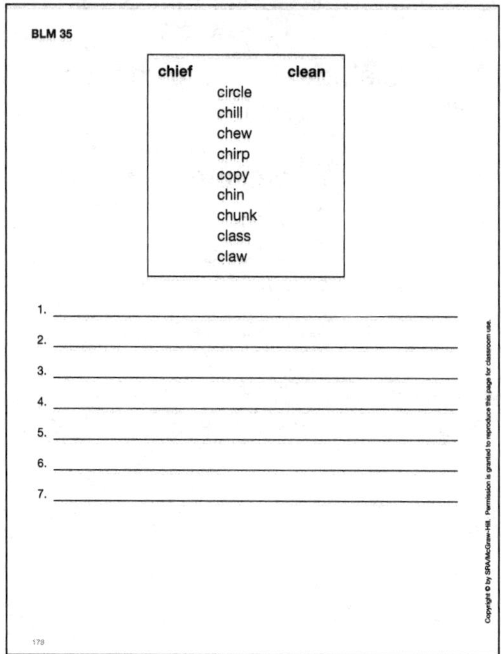

BLM 35

chief	clean

circle
chill
chew
chirp
copy
chin
chunk
class
claw

1. ________
2. ________
3. ________
4. ________
5. ________
6. ________
7. ________

178

1. (Hand out BLM 35.)
   - The words at the top are **chief** and **clean.** Everybody, which word comes earlier in the alphabet? (Signal.) *Chief.*
2. Seven of the words below **chief** and **clean** come between them in the alphabet. Write the seven words in alphabetical order. Raise your hand when you're finished.
   (Observe students and give feedback.)
3. (Write on the board:)

   1. chill
   2. chin
   3. chirp
   4. chunk
   5. circle
   6. class
   7. claw

   - Check your work. Here's what you should have. Fix up any mistakes.

Extension Lesson 36

Materials: Each student will need a copy of BLM 36A and BLM 36B.

Objective A: **Locate and alphabetize words in a glossary.**

Objective B: Alphabetize words between guide words.

EXERCISE A

GLOSSARY AND GUIDE WORDS

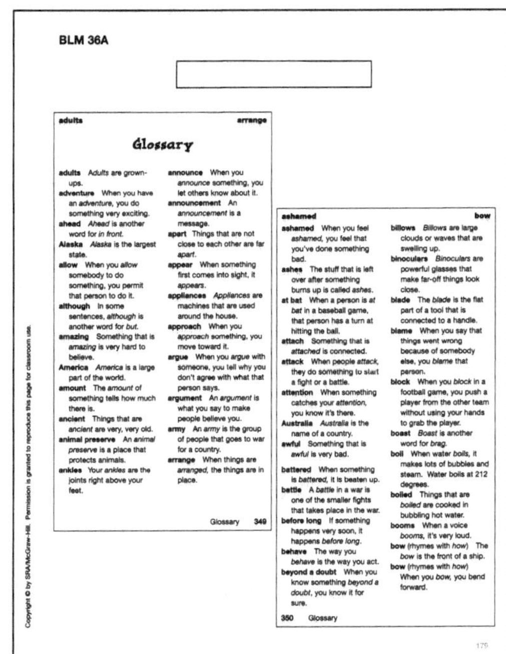

BLM 36A

adults **arrange**

Glossary

adults *Adults* are grown-ups.
adventure When you have an *adventure*, you do something very exciting.
ahead *Ahead* is another word for *in front.*
Alaska *Alaska* is the largest state.
allow When you *allow* somebody to do something, you permit that person to do it.
although In some sentences, *although* is another word for *but.*
amazing Something that is *amazing* is very hard to believe.
America *America* is a large part of the world.
amount The *amount* of something tells how much there is.
ancient Things that are *ancient* are very, very old.
animal preserve An *animal preserve* is a place that protects animals.
ankles Your *ankles* are the joints right above your feet.
announce When you *announce* something, you let others know about it.
announcement An *announcement* is a message.
apart Things that are not close to each other are far *apart.*
appear When something first comes into sight, it *appears.*
appliances *Appliances* are machines that are used around the house.
approach When you *approach* something, you move toward it.
argue When you *argue* with someone, you tell why you don't agree with what that person says.
argument An *argument* is what you say to make people believe you.
army An *army* is the group of people that goes to war for a country.
arrange When things are *arranged*, the things are in place.

Glossary 349

ashamed **bow**

ashamed When you feel *ashamed*, you feel that you've done something bad.
ashes The stuff that is left over after something burns up is called *ashes.*
at bat When a person is *at bat* in a baseball game, that person has a turn at hitting the ball.
attach Something that is *attached* is connected.
attack When people *attack*, they do something to start a fight or a battle.
attention When something catches your *attention*, you know it's there.
Australia *Australia* is the name of a country.
awful Something that is *awful* is very bad.
battered When something is *battered*, it is beaten up.
battle A *battle* in a war is one of the smaller fights that takes place in the war.
before long If something happens very soon, it happens *before long.*
behave The way you *behave* is the way you act.
beyond a doubt When you know something *beyond a doubt*, you know it for sure.
billows *Billows* are large clouds or waves that are swelling up.
binoculars *Binoculars* are powerful glasses that make far-off things look close.
blade The *blade* is the flat part of a tool that is connected to a handle.
blame When you say that things went wrong because of somebody else, you *blame* that person.
block When you *block* in a football game, you push a player from the other team without using your hands to grab the player.
boast *Boast* is another word for *brag.*
boil When water *boils*, it makes lots of bubbles and steam. Water boils at 212 degrees.
boiled Things that are *boiled* are cooked in bubbling hot water.
booms When a voice *booms*, it's very loud.
bow (rhymes with *how*) The *bow* is the front of a ship.
bow (rhymes with *how*) When you *bow*, you bend forward.

350 Glossary

179

1. (Hand out sample glossaries to the students [BLM 36A].)
- These are glossaries from the back of a textbook. You'll use glossaries to find words and do other exercises.
- Find page 349 in your glossary. A glossary gives meanings of words that are used in a book. The words are in alphabetical order. The two words at the top of each page are called guide words.

2. The first guide word on page 349 is **adults.** Everybody, touch that guide word. ✔
- That tells that the first word on page 349 is **adults.**
- Touch the other guide word for page 349. ✔
- Everybody, what's that guide word? (Signal.) *Arrange.*
- That tells that the last word on page 349 is **arrange.**

3. Find page 350. ✔
- Page 350 has two guide words. Everybody, touch the first guide word on that page. ✔
- What's the first guide word? (Signal.) *Ashamed.*
- So what's the first word on page 350? (Signal.) *Ashamed.*
- What's the second guide word on page 350? (Call on a student. Accept *bow* or *bōw*.)
- Everybody, so what's the last word on that page? (Signal.) *Bow.*

4. (Write on the board:)

asteroid

- Let's say I want to add the word **asteroid** to the glossary. Would I add **asteroid** to page 349 or to page 350? (Wait.) What page? (Signal.) *350.*
- Yes, **asteroid** comes between **ashamed** and **bow** in the alphabet.

5. Your turn. Copy the word **asteroid.** Write it in the box at the top of your worksheet. ✔
- Now draw an arrow to show where the word **asteroid** would go in the glossary. Draw that arrow between two words. Raise your hand when you're finished. (Observe students and give feedback.)
- Everybody, name the word that comes just before where **asteroid** goes. (Signal.) *Ashes.*
- Yes, **asteroid** comes between **ashes** and **at bat** in the alphabet.

EXERCISE B

GLOSSARY AND GUIDE WORDS

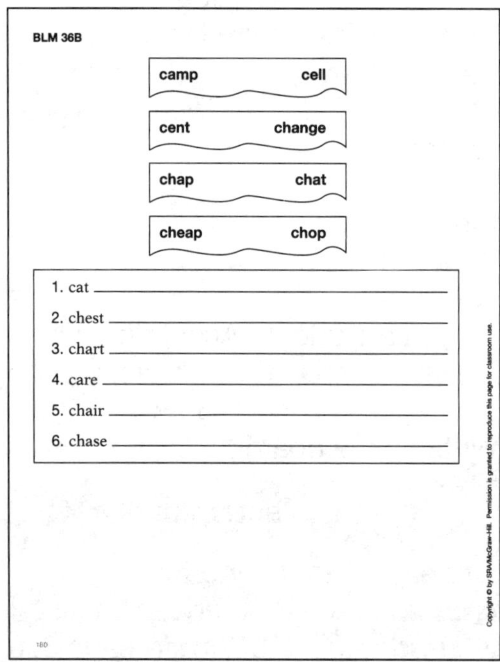
BLM 36B

camp	cell
cent	change
chap	chat
cheap	chop

1. cat ____
2. chest ____
3. chart ____
4. care ____
5. chair ____
6. chase ____

1. (Hand out BLM 36B.)
- Each row shows two guide words for pages in a glossary. The first guide words are **camp** and **cell.** The next guide words are **cent** and **change.** Then the next guide words are **chap** and **chat.** The last guide words are **cheap** and **chop.**

2. In the box below the guide words is a list of six words. Each of those words would go on a page that has one pair of the guide words. After each word on your paper, you'll write the guide words for the page where you would find that word in the glossary.
- Word 1 is **cat. Cat** is between one pair of guide words. Find that pair and write them after the word **cat.** Raise your hand when you've done that much. (Observe students and give feedback.)
- Check your work. Everybody, what are the guide words for the word **cat**? (Signal.) *Camp and cell.*
- Yes, **cat** is between **camp** and **cell** in the alphabet.

3. Word 2 is **chest.** Figure out the guide words for the page where you'd find **chest** and write them after the word **chest**. Then do the guide words for the rest of the items. Raise your hand when you're finished. (Observe students and give feedback.)

4. (Write on the board:)

1. cat	**camp**	**cell**
2. chest	**cheap**	**chop**
3. chart	**chap**	**chat**
4. care	**camp**	**cell**
5. chair	**cent**	**change**
6. chase	**chap**	**chat**

- Check your work. Here's what you should have. Fix up any mistakes.

Extension Lesson 37

Materials: Each student will need a copy of BLM 37.

Objective: Alphabetize words between guide words.

GUIDE WORDS

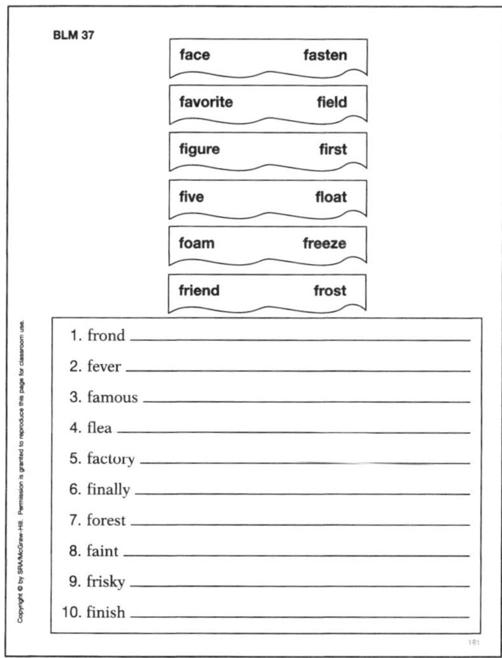

BLM 37

face	fasten
favorite	field
figure	first
five	float
foam	freeze
friend	frost

1. frond ____
2. fever ____
3. famous ____
4. flea ____
5. factory ____
6. finally ____
7. forest ____
8. faint ____
9. frisky ____
10. finish ____

1. (Hand out BLM 37.)
   - Your worksheet shows guide words for six pages of a glossary. In the box are ten words that go on these pages.
2. After each word, write the guide words for the page where you would find the word in a glossary. Raise your hand when you're finished.
   (Observe students and give feedback.)

Key:

1. frond — friend frost
2. fever — favorite field
3. famous — face fasten
4. flea — five float
5. factory — face fasten
6. finally — figure first
7. forest — foam freeze
8. faint — face fasten
9. frisky — friend frost
10. finish — figure first

Extension Lesson 38

Materials: Each student will need a copy of BLM 38.

Objective: Alphabetize words between guide words.

GUIDE WORDS

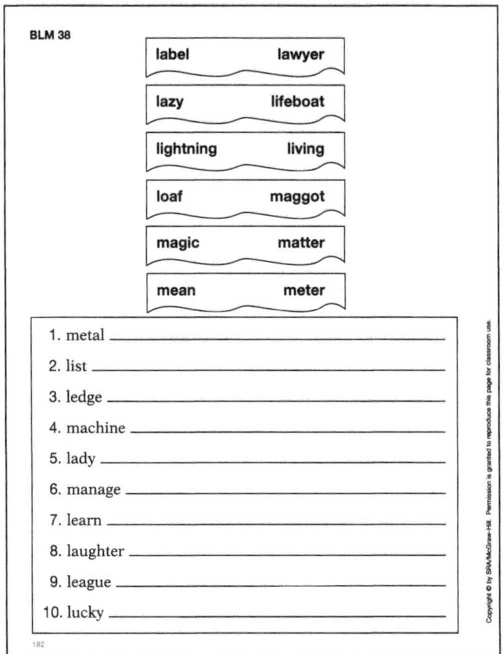
BLM 38

label	lawyer
lazy	lifeboat
lightning	living
loaf	maggot
magic	matter
mean	meter

1. metal ______
2. list ______
3. ledge ______
4. machine ______
5. lady ______
6. manage ______
7. learn ______
8. laughter ______
9. league ______
10. lucky ______

182

1. (Hand out BLM 38.)
- Your worksheet shows guide words for six pages of a glossary. In the box are ten words that go on these pages.
2. After each word, write the guide words for the page where you would find the word in the glossary. Raise your hand when you're finished.
(Observe students and give feedback.)

Key:

1. metal mean meter
2. list lightning living
3. ledge lazy lifeboat
4. machine loaf maggot
5. lady label lawyer
6. manage magic matter
7. learn lazy lifeboat
8. laughter label lawyer
9. league lazy lifeboat
10. lucky loaf maggot

Note: For Extension Lessons 39, 40 and 41, teacher and each student will need the same edition of a children's dictionary.

Extension Lesson 39

Materials: Teacher and each student will need the same children's dictionary and lined paper.

Objective: **Use a dictionary to look up the meanings of words.**

DICTIONARY SKILLS

1. (Hold up a dictionary.)
- This is a dictionary. It tells what words mean.
- The words in a dictionary are in alphabetical order. The words on the first pages of the dictionary begin with **A.** The words at the end of the dictionary begin with **Z.**

2. Each page has guide words at the top. Open your dictionary to page 100. ✔
- Everybody, what are the guide words for page 100? (Signal.) (Accept appropriate response.)
- Open your dictionary to page 200. ✔
- What are the guide words for page 200? (Signal.) (Accept appropriate response.)
- What are the guide words for page 201? (Signal.) (Accept appropriate response.)

3. (Write on the board:)

1. descend

- This word is **descend.** Number your paper from 1 through 3. Then copy the word **descend** on your paper.
- I'll use **descend** in a sentence: They will descend the hill. From that sentence, you don't know exactly what the word means. It could mean go up the hill or it could mean go down the hill. Or it could mean they will eat the hill.
- Look up the word **descend** in the dictionary and read what is says after the word **descend.** Don't pay any attention to the letters and funny marks that come after the word **descend.** Just keep reading and you'll find out what **descend** means. You don't have to read the whole thing. Then write what **descend** means. Write whether **descend** means **go up, go down, go sideways** or something else.
(Observe students and give feedback.)
- What does **descend** mean? (Call on a student. Idea: *Go down.*)
- Everybody, touch the word **descend** in the dictionary. ✔
- I'll read the sentence that tells what **descend** means. (Read the first definition.)

4. (Write on the board:)

2. harrow

- **Harrow** is the next word you'll look up. Copy it on your paper.
- I'll use **harrow** in a sentence: The farmer came home with an old harrow. A harrow could be an animal, a tool or a person. Look up **harrow** and write whether it's an animal, a tool or a person.
(Observe students and give feedback.)
- Everybody, is a harrow a tool, an animal or a person? (Signal.) *A tool.*

5. (Write on the board:)

3. lavish

- The last word you'll look up is **lavish.** I'll use **lavish** in a sentence: Her house was very lavish. **Lavish** could mean **small** or **large,** or it could be much more house than she needs. Copy the word **lavish.** Look it up and write what it means.
(Observe students and give feedback.)

- Everybody, does **lavish** mean **small, large** or **more than someone needs?** (Signal.) *More than someone needs.*

Extension Lesson 40

Materials: Teacher and each student will need the same children's dictionary and lined paper.

Objective: Use a dictionary to look up the meanings of words.

DICTIONARY SKILLS

1. (Hold up a dictionary.)
- Everybody, what kind of book is this? (Signal.) *Dictionary.*
- The dictionary gives meanings of words. Remember, the words in a dictionary are in alphabetical order. The words on the first pages of the dictionary begin with **A.** The words at the end of the dictionary begin with **Z.**

2. (Write on the board:)

1. macaw

- This word is **macaw.** Number your paper from 1 through 3. Then copy the word **macaw** on your paper. ✔
- I'll use **macaw** in a sentence: They saw a macaw in the jungle. From that sentence, you don't know exactly what the word means. A macaw could be a large tree, a colorful bird or a kind of pond. Look up the word **macaw** in the dictionary and read what it says after the word **macaw.** Then write what **macaw** means.
(Observe students and give feedback.)

3. Everybody, what is a macaw? (Signal.) *A bird.*
- Touch the word **macaw** in the dictionary. ✔
- I'll read the sentence that tells what a macaw is. (Read the first definition.)

4. (Write on the board:)

2. oddment

- The next word you'll look up is **oddment.** Copy it on your paper. ✔
- I'll use **oddment** in a sentence: They had a lot of oddments after they finished the dinner. Oddments could be stomach pains, dirty dishes or leftover food. Look up **oddment** and write what it is.
(Observe students and give feedback.)
- Everybody, are oddments stomach pains, dirty dishes or leftovers? (Signal.) *Leftovers.*

5. (Write on the board:)

3. raiment

- The last word you'll look up is **raiment.** I'll use **raiment** in a sentence: Their raiment was stolen. Their raiment could be their luggage or their clothing or their animal. Copy the word **raiment.** Then look it up and write what it means.
(Observe students and give feedback.)
- Everybody, is raiment their luggage, their clothing or their animal? (Signal.) *Their clothing.*

Extension Lesson 41

Materials: Teacher and each student will need the same children's dictionary and lined paper.

Objective: Use a dictionary to look up the meanings of words.

DICTIONARY SKILLS

1. (Hold up a dictionary.)
- Everybody, what kind of book is this? (Signal.) *Dictionary.*
- You're going to look up words and write what they mean.

2. (Write on the board:)

1. sanction

- This word is **sanction.** Number your paper from 1 through 3. Then copy the word **sanction** on your paper. ✔
- I'll use **sanction** in a sentence: The mayor sanctioned our plan. From that sentence, you don't know exactly what the word means. The mayor could approve of our plan, fight our plan or pay no attention to our plan.
- Look up the word **sanction** in the dictionary and write whether the mayor approved of our plan, fought the plan or paid no attention to the plan. (Observe students and give feedback.)

3. Everybody, if the mayor sanctioned the plan, what did the mayor do? (Signal.) *Approved of the plan.*
- I'll read the sentence in the dictionary that tells what the mayor did. (Read the first definition for the **verb** sanction.)

4. (Write on the board:)

2. velocity

- The next word you'll look up is **velocity.** What word? (Signal.) *Velocity.*
- Copy it on your paper. ✔
- I'll use **velocity** in a sentence: The plane had a lot of velocity. From that sentence, **velocity** could mean that the plane had a lot of fuel, a lot of passengers or a lot of speed. Look up **velocity** and write what it means. (Observe students and give feedback.)
- Everybody, did the plane have a lot of fuel, a lot of passengers or a lot of speed? (Signal.) *A lot of speed.*

5. (Write on the board:)

3. diminutive

- The last word you'll look up is **diminutive.** What word? (Signal.) *Diminutive.*
- I'll use **diminutive** in a sentence: His daughter was quite diminutive. From that sentence, she could be very small, very quiet or very pretty. Look up **diminutive** and write what it means. (Observe students and give feedback.)
- Everybody, was his daughter very small, very quiet or very pretty? (Signal.) *Very small.*

Extension Lesson 42

Materials: Each student will need a copy of BLM 42.

Objective: Alphabetize words (mixed set).

ALPHABETICAL ORDER

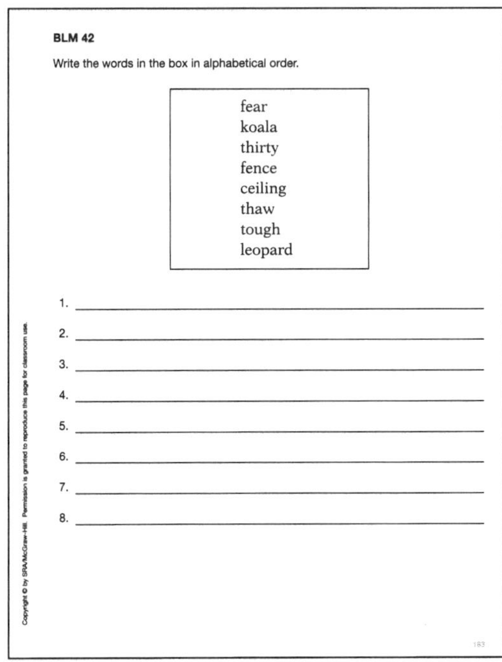

BLM 42

Write the words in the box in alphabetical order.

fear
koala
thirty
fence
ceiling
thaw
tough
leopard

1. ______
2. ______
3. ______
4. ______
5. ______
6. ______
7. ______
8. ______

1. (Hand out BLM 42.)
- You're going to put these words in alphabetical order. Figure out which word is the first in the list and write it. Then cross it out in your box. Raise your hand when you're finished. (Observe students and give feedback.)

2. (Write on the board:)

1. ceiling

- Here's what you should have for word 1: **ceiling.**

3. Complete the list. Remember to cross out each word when you write it in your list.
4. (Write to show:)

1. ceiling
2. fear
3. fence
4. koala
5. leopard
6. thaw
7. thirty
8. tough

- Check your work. Here's the list you should have. Fix up any mistakes. (Observe students and give feedback.)

Extension Lesson 43

Materials: Each student will need a copy of BLM 43.

Objective: Alphabetize words between guide words.

GUIDE WORDS

BLM 43

Write the guide words for the page where you would find that word in a glossary.

pack	paint
palm	paper
pardon	paw

1. pass ____________
2. page ____________
3. patch ____________
4. panel ____________

184

Key:

1. pass pardon paw
2. page pack paint
3. patch pardon paw
4. panel palm paper

1. (Hand out BLM 43.)
- Your worksheet shows guide words for three pages of a glossary. In the box are four words that go on these pages.
2. After each word, write the guide words for the page where you would find the word in a glossary. Raise your hand when you're finished.
(Observe students and give feedback.)

Extension Lesson 44

Materials: Each student will need a copy of BLM 44.

Objective: Alphabetize words that start with different letters.

ALPHABETICAL ORDER

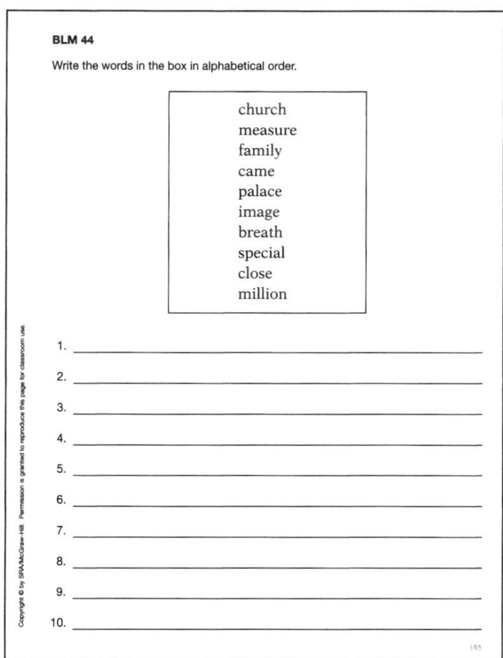

BLM 44

Write the words in the box in alphabetical order.

church
measure
family
came
palace
image
breath
special
close
million

1. ______
2. ______
3. ______
4. ______
5. ______
6. ______
7. ______
8. ______
9. ______
10. ______

185

1. (Hand out BLM 44.)
- You're going to put these ten words in alphabetical order. Figure out which word is the first in the list and write it. Raise your hand when you're finished. (Observe students and give feedback.)

2. (Write on the board:)

1. breath

- Here's what you should have for word 1: **breath.**

3. Complete the list. Remember to cross out each word when you write it in your list.
4. (Write to show:)

1. breath
2. came
3. church
4. close
5. family
6. image
7. measure
8. million
9. palace
10. special

- Check your work. Here's the list you should have. Fix up any mistakes.

Extension Lesson 45

Materials: Each student will need a copy of BLM 45.

Objective: **Construct a set of directions for making a figure.**

CONSTRUCTING DIRECTIONS

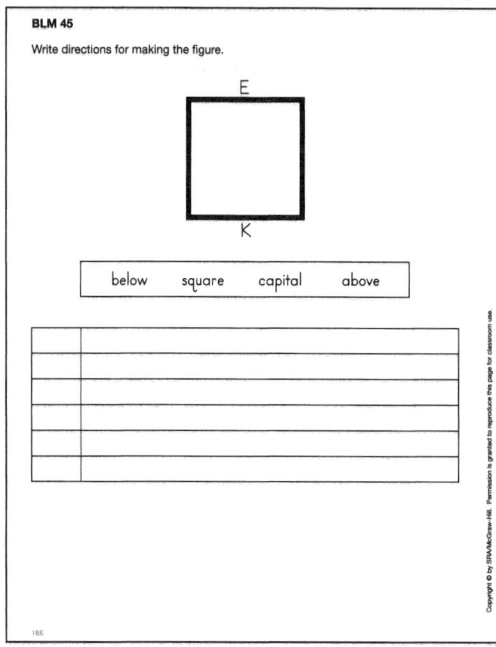
BLM 45

Write directions for making the figure.

E

K

below square capital above

Copyright © by SRA/McGraw-Hill. Permission is granted to reproduce this page for classroom use.

186

1. (Hand out BLM 45.)
- You're going to write directions for making a figure.
2. You're going to write directions so that somebody would be able to make this figure. The main part of this figure is a square. What's the main part? (Signal.) *A square.*
- What's just above the square? (Signal.) *E.*
- What's just below the square? (Signal.) *K.*
- What's the main part of this figure? (Signal.) *A square.*
3. Here's a sentence that tells how to make the main part of the figure: Make a large square.
- Everybody, write that sentence. ✔
4. Now write a sentence that tells about making the **E.** Tell what to make and where to make it. Raise your hand when you've written about the main part and about the **E.**
(Observe students and give feedback.)
- Check your work. Here are good sentences for the main part and the **E:** Make a square. Make an **E** just above the square.
- Here's a sentence about the **E** that is not as good, but it's okay: Make an **E** above the square. That doesn't tell that it is **just** above the square. So it could be anywhere above the square. It's better to say: Make an **E** just above the square.
(Call on different students to read their first two sentences.)
5. Everybody, write your sentence for the **K.** Raise your hand when you've written about the **K.**
(Observe students and give feedback.)
- Check your work. Here's a good sentence for the **K:** Make a **K** just below the square.
(Call on different students to read their sentence for the **K.**)
6. (Call on different students to read all of their sentences. Tell how to rewrite parts that are not clear or are incorrect.)
7. Fix up your sentences so that you have written good directions for making the figure. Raise your hand when you're finished.
(Observe students and give feedback.)

Extension Lesson 46

Materials: Each student will need a copy of BLM 46.

Objective: Construct a set of directions for making a figure.

CONSTRUCTING DIRECTIONS

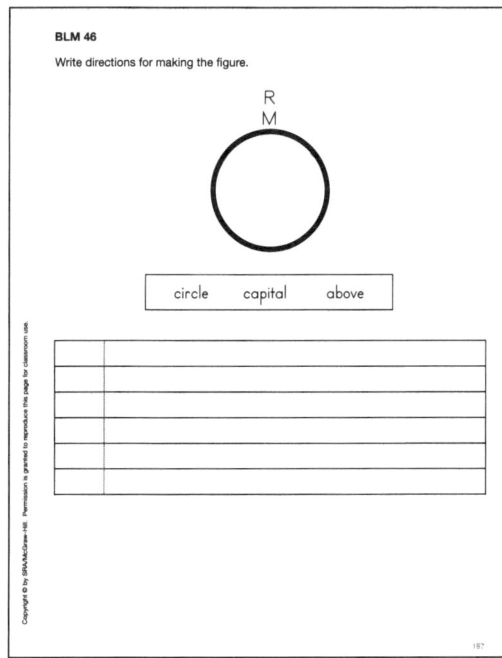

1. (Hand out BLM 46.)
- You're going to write directions for making a figure.
2. You're going to write directions so that somebody would be able to make this figure. The parts of this figure are an **R,** an **M** and a circle.
- What's the main part of the figure? (Signal.) *A circle.*
- What's just above the circle? (Signal.) *M.*
- What's just above the **M**? (Signal.) *R.*
3. Write your sentence for making the main part of the figure. Raise your hand when you're finished.
(Observe students and give feedback.)
- Read your sentence. (Call on a student. Idea: *Make a large circle.*)
4. You're going to write sentences that tell about making the **R** and the **M.** First you write about the letter that is closest to the main part.
- Which letter are you going to write about first? (Signal.) *M.*
Yes, the **M.**
- Write your sentences for the **M** and for the **R.** Raise your hand when you're finished.
(Observe students and give feedback.)
- Read both your sentences. (Call on different students. Ideas: *Make an M just above the circle. Make an R just above the M.*)
5. Read your directions for making the whole figure. (Call on different students to read their directions. Tell how to rewrite parts that are not clear or are incorrect.)
6. Fix up your sentences so that you have written good directions for making the figure. Raise your hand when you're finished.
(Observe students and give feedback.)
7. Remember how you wrote your directions. First you told about the main part. Then you told about the part that is closest to the main part.

Extension Lesson 47

Materials: Each student will need a copy of BLM 47.

Objective: Construct a set of directions for making a figure.

CONSTRUCTING DIRECTIONS

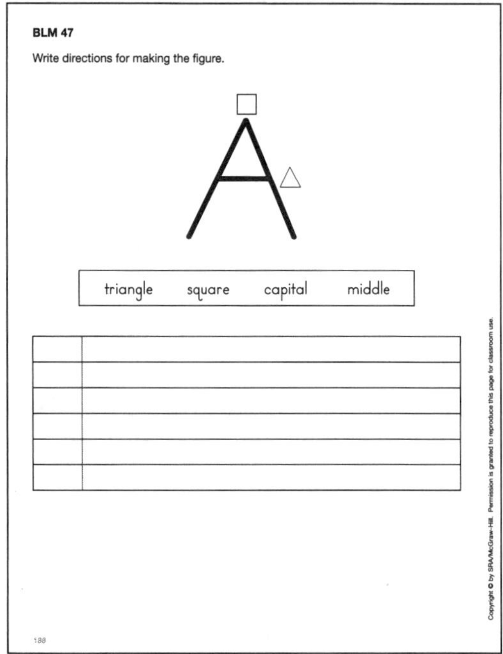

BLM 47

Write directions for making the figure.

triangle square capital middle

1. (Hand out BLM 47.)
- You're going to write directions for making a figure.

2. You're going to write directions so that somebody would be able to make this figure. The parts of this figure are a square, an **A** and a triangle.
- What's the main part of the figure? (Signal.) *An A.*
- What's just above the capital **A**? (Signal.) *A square.*
- Where is the triangle? (Call on different students. Idea: *Just to the right of the A; just to the right of the bar for the A; just to the right of the middle of the A.*) Yes, the triangle is just to the right of the middle of the **A.**

3. Write your sentence for the main part of the figure. Raise your hand when you're finished.
(Observe students and give feedback.)
- Read your sentence. (Call on a student. Idea: *Make a large A.*)

4. Write a sentence that tells about making the square and a sentence that tells about making the triangle. Make sure you give enough information so that somebody would know exactly where to make the triangle. Raise your hand when you're finished.
(Observe students and give feedback.)
- Read both your sentences. (Call on different students. Ideas: *Make a square just above the A. Make a triangle just to the right of the middle of the A.*)

5. Read your directions for making the whole figure. (Call on different students to read their directions. Give feedback on parts that are good. Tell how to rewrite parts that are not clear or are incorrect.)

6. Fix up your sentences so that you have written good directions for making the figure. Raise your hand when you're finished.
(Observe students and give feedback.)

Materials: Each student will need a copy of BLM 48.

Objective: Construct a set of directions for making a figure.

CONSTRUCTING DIRECTIONS

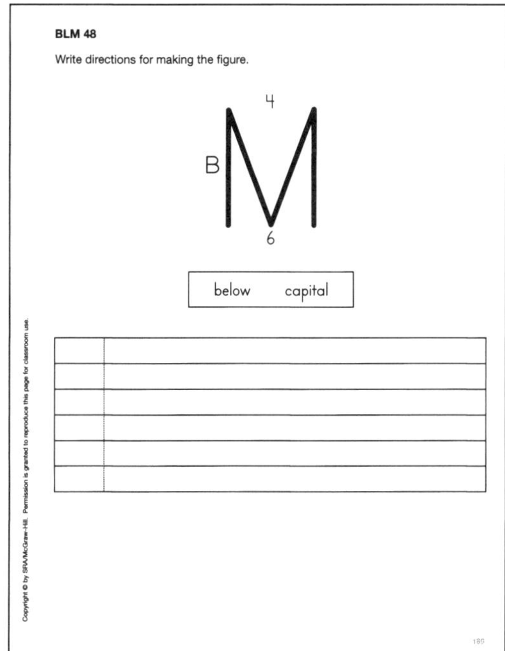
BLM 48

Write directions for making the figure.

1. (Hand out BLM 48.)
- You're going to write directions for making figures.

2. You're going to write directions so that somebody would be able to make this figure. The parts are a **B,** a capital **M,** a **4** and a **6.**
- What's the main part of the figure? (Signal.) *M.*
- What's just above the **M**? (Signal.) *4.*
- Where is the **B**? (Call on a student. Idea: *Just to the left of the middle of the M.*)
- Where is the **6**? (Call on a student. Idea: *Just below the M.*)

3. Write your sentence for the main part of the figure. Raise your hand when you're finished.
(Observe students and give feedback.)
- Read your sentence. (Call on a student. Idea: *Make a large M.*)

4. Write a sentence for each of the other things in the figure. Write your sentences for **4, B** and **6.** Raise your hand when you're finished.
(Observe students and give feedback.)
- (Call on different students to read their sentences. Ideas: *Make a small 4 just above [the middle of] the M. Make a small B just to the left of the middle of the M. Make a small 6 just below [the middle of] the M.*)

5. Read your directions for making the whole figure. (Call on different students to read their directions. Give feedback on parts that are good. Tell how to rewrite parts that are not clear or are incorrect.)

6. Fix up your sentences so that you have written good directions for making the figure. Raise your hand when you're finished.
(Observe students and give feedback.)

Materials: Each student will need a copy of BLM 49.

Objective: Construct a set of directions for making a figure.

CONSTRUCTING DIRECTIONS

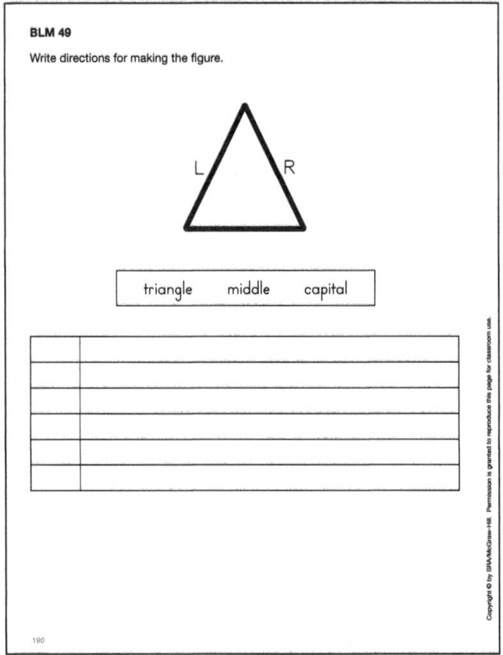
BLM 49

Write directions for making the figure.

triangle middle capital

190

1. (Hand out BLM 49.)
- You're going to write directions for making figures.
2. You're going to write directions so that somebody would be able to make this figure. The parts are a capital **L,** a triangle and a capital **R.**
- What's the main part of the figure? (Signal.) *A triangle.*
- Where is the **L**? (Call on a student. Idea: *Just to the left of the middle of the triangle.*)
- Where is the **R**? (Call on a student. Idea: *Just to the right of the middle of the triangle.*)
3. Write your sentence for the main part of the figure. Raise your hand when you're finished. (Observe students and give feedback.)
- Read your sentence. (Call on different students. Idea: *Make a large triangle; make a large triangle with a point on top.*)
4. Write a sentence for each of the other things in the figure. Raise your hand when you're finished. (Observe students and give feedback.)
- Read your sentences. (Call on different students to read their sentences. Ideas: *Make an L just left of the middle of the triangle. Make an R just right of the middle of the triangle.*)
5. Read your directions for making the whole figure. (Call on different students to read their directions. Give feedback on parts that are good. Tell how to rewrite parts that are not clear or are incorrect.)
6. Fix up your sentences so that you have written good directions for making the figure. Raise your hand when you're finished. (Observe students and give feedback.)

Extension Lesson 50

Materials: Each student will need a copy of BLM 50.

Objective: Construct a set of directions for making a figure.

CONSTRUCTING DIRECTIONS

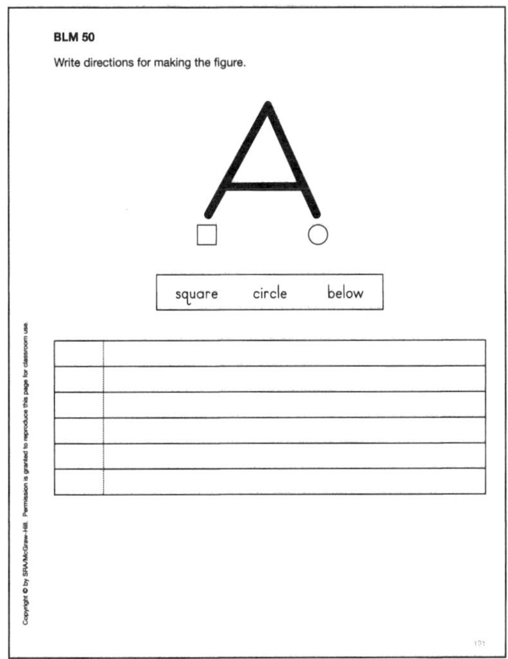
BLM 50

Write directions for making the figure.

1. (Hand out BLM 50.)
• You're going to write directions for making a figure.
2. You're going to write directions so that somebody would be able to make this figure.
• What's the main part of the figure? (Signal.) *A.*
• Where is the square? (Call on a student. Idea: *Just below the left line.*)
• Where is the circle? (Call on a student. Idea: *Just below the right line.*)
3. Write your sentences for making the figure. Remember to start with the directions for making the main part. Raise your hand when you're finished. (Observe students and give feedback.)
4. Read your directions for making the whole figure. (Call on different students to read their directions. Give feedback on parts that are good. Tell how to rewrite parts that are not clear or are incorrect.)

   Key:
   - *Make a large A.*
   - *Make a square just below the left line.*
   - *Make a circle just below the right line.*
5. Fix up your sentences so that you have written good directions for making the figure. ✔

Extension Lesson 51

Materials: Each student will need a copy of BLM 51.

Objective A: **Identify a horizontal line.**

Objective B: Construct a set of directions for making a figure.

EXERCISE A

IDENTIFY HORIZONTAL LINE

1. (Draw a horizontal line on the board:)

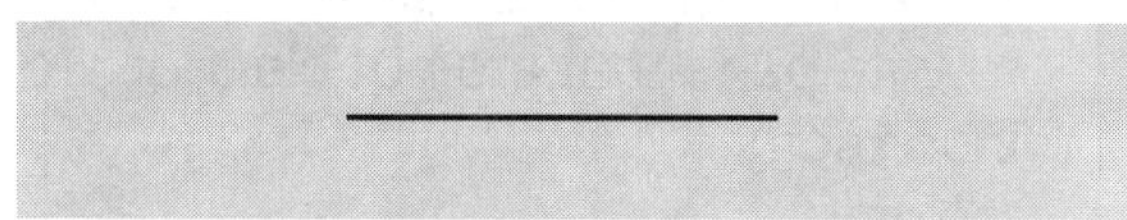

- This is a line. It is a horizontal line. A horizontal line does not go up and down; it goes from side to side.

2. (Draw a slanted line:)

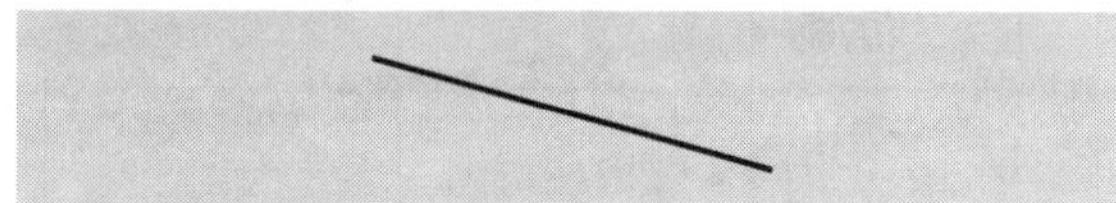

- This line is not horizontal.

3. (Draw a vertical line:)

- This line is not horizontal.

4. (Point to the horizontal line.) What kind of line is this? (Signal.) *Horizontal.*

EXERCISE B

CONSTRUCTING DIRECTIONS

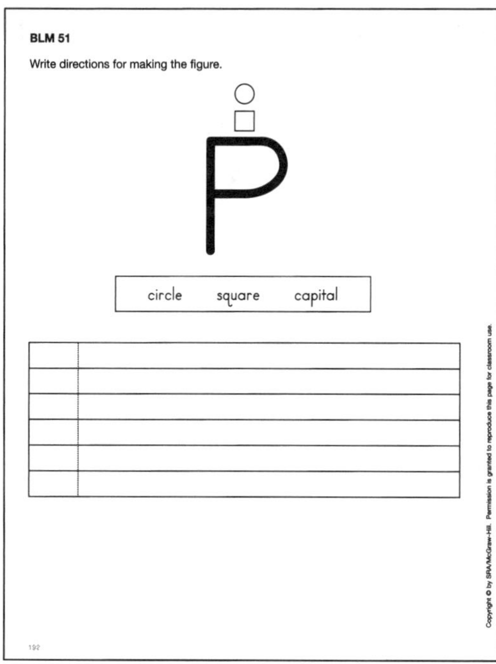

BLM 51

Write directions for making the figure.

circle square capital

192

1. (Hand out BLM 51.)

- You're going to write directions so that somebody would be able to make this figure. The parts are a **P,** a square and a circle.
- What's the main part of the figure? (Signal.) *P.*
- What's just over the **P**? (Signal.) *A square.*
- Where is the circle? (Call on a student. Idea: *Just over the square.*)

2. Write your sentences for making the figure. Remember to start with the directions for making the main part. Raise your hand when you're finished. (Observe students and give feedback.)

3. Read your directions for making the whole figure. (Call on several students to read their directions. Give feedback on parts that are good. Tell how to rewrite parts that are not clear or are incorrect.)

   Key:
   - *Make a large P.*
   - *Make a small square just over the P.*
   - *Make a small circle just over the square.*

4. Fix up your sentences so that you have written good directions for making the figure. ✔

Materials: Each student will need a copy of BLM 52.

Objective A: Identify a horizontal line.

Objective B: Construct a set of directions for making a figure.

EXERCISE A

IDENTIFY HORIZONTAL LINE

- (Draw a horizontal line on the board.) What kind of line is this? (Signal.) *Horizontal.*

EXERCISE B

CONSTRUCTING DIRECTIONS

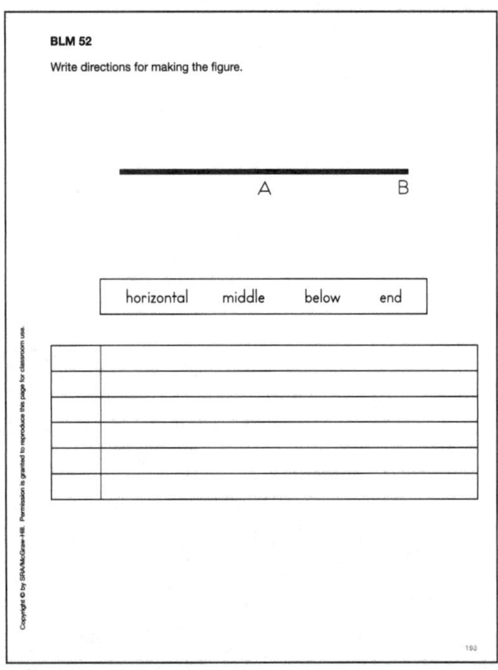

BLM 52

Write directions for making the figure.

A B

horizontal	middle	below	end

Copyright © by SRA/McGraw-Hill. Permission is granted to reproduce this page for classroom use.

193

1. (Hand out BLM 52.)
- You're going to write directions so that somebody would be able to make this figure.
- What's the main part of the figure? (Signal.) *Horizontal line.*
- Where is the **A**? (Call on a student. Idea: *Just below the middle of the horizontal line.*)
- Where is the **B**? (Call on a student. Idea: *Just below the right end of the line.*)

2. Write your directions for making the figure. Raise your hand when you're finished.
   (Observe students and give feedback.)
3. Read your directions for making the whole figure. (Call on several students to read their directions. Give feedback on parts that are good. Tell how to rewrite parts that are not clear or are incorrect.)

   Key:
   - *Make a horizontal line.*
   - *Make an A just below the middle of the [horizontal] line.*
   - *Make a B just below the right end of the line.*
4. Fix up your sentences so that you have written good directions for making the figure. ✔

Extension Lesson 53

Materials: Each student will need a copy of BLM 53.

Objective: Construct a set of directions for making a figure.

CONSTRUCTING DIRECTIONS

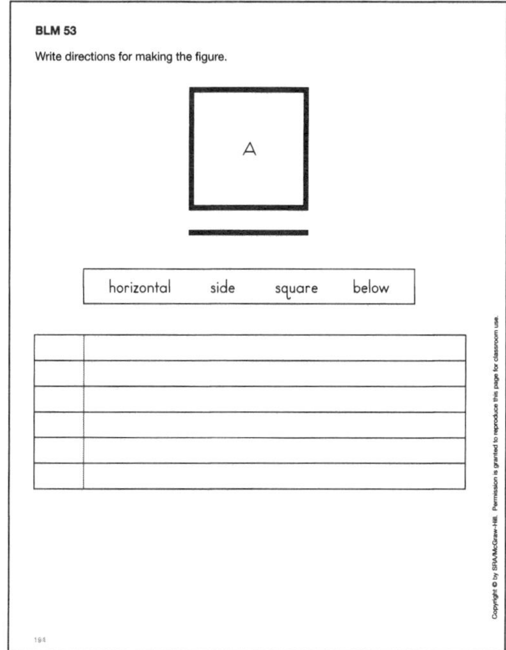

1. (Hand out BLM 53.)
- This is a tough figure to describe. You're going to have to tell where to make the horizontal line and how long it should be.
- What's the main part of this figure? (Signal.) *A square.*
- Where is the **A**? (Call on a student. Idea: *In the middle of the square.*)
- Where is the horizontal line? (Call on a student. Idea: *Just below the square.*)

2. Listen: The horizontal line goes from the left side of the square. Say that. (Signal.) *The horizontal line goes from the left side of the square.*
- Where does the horizontal line go **to**? (Signal.) *The right side of the square.*
- Listen: The horizontal line goes from the left side of the square to the right side of the square. Say that. (Signal.) *The horizontal line goes from the left side of the square to the right side of the square.*
(Repeat step 2 until firm.)

3. Write your directions for the square and the **A.** Raise your hand when you've done that much.
(Observe students and give feedback.)
- (Call on several students to read what they have written. Ideas: *Make a square. Make a capital A in the middle of the square.*)

4. You're going to write two sentences about the horizontal line. First you'll tell where to make it. Then you'll tell where it should start and where it should end.
- Write your sentence about where to make a horizontal line. Raise your hand when you're finished.
(Observe students and give feedback.)
- Read your sentence. (Call on a student. Idea: *Make a horizontal line just below the square.*)
- Now write a sentence that says **make the horizontal line go from . . .** and tells what side of the square it goes from and what side it goes to. Raise your hand when you're finished.
(Observe students and give feedback.)
- Read your sentence. (Call on a student. Idea: *Make the horizontal line go from the left side of the square* ***to the right side of the square.***)

5. Read your directions for making the whole figure. (Call on several students. Give feedback on parts that are good. Tell how to rewrite the parts that are not clear or are incorrect.)

6. Fix up your sentences so that you have written good directions for making the figure. ✔

Extension Lesson 54

Materials: Each student will need a copy of BLM 54.

Objective: Construct a set of directions for making a figure.

CONSTRUCTING DIRECTIONS

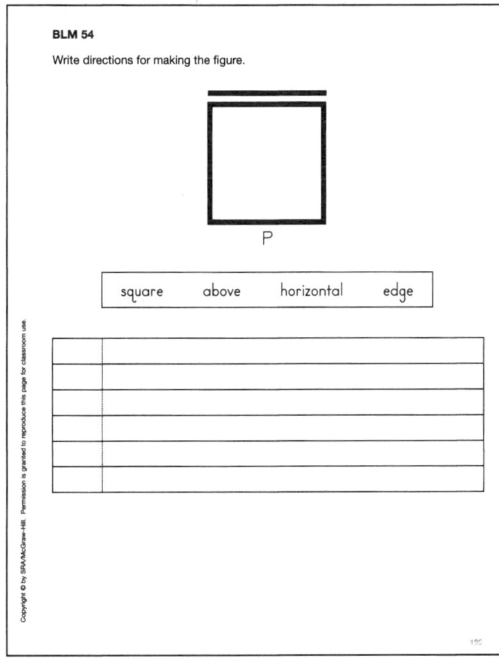

BLM 54

Write directions for making the figure.

P

square above horizontal edge

1. (Hand out BLM 54.)
   - You're going to write directions so that somebody would be able to make this figure.
   - What's the main part of the figure? (Signal.) *A square.*
   - What's just below the middle of the square? (Signal.) *P.*
   - Where is the horizontal line? (Call on a student. Idea: *Just above the square.*)
   - You'll need two sentences to tell about the horizontal line. So you'll write your directions for the horizontal line last.
2. Start with the sentence for the square. Then write the directions for the **P.** Then write the directions for the horizontal line. Remember, first tell where the line is. Then tell that you make the line go from the left side of the square to the right side of the square. Write your sentences for the figure. Raise your hand when you're finished.
   (Observe students and give feedback.)
3. Read your directions for making the whole figure. (Call on several students. Idea: *Make a large square. Make a P just below the middle of the square. Make a horizontal line just above the square. Make the [horizontal] line go from the left side of the square to the right side of the square.*)
4. (Give feedback on parts that are good. Tell how to rewrite the parts that are not clear or are incorrect.)
5. Fix up your sentences so that you have written good directions for making the figure. ✔

Extension Lesson 55

Materials: Each student will need lined paper.
Objective A: **Reconstruct a dictated passage.**
Objective B: **Rewrite [and illustrate] the story.**

EXERCISE A

RETELLING

1. I'll tell a story twice. Then I'll call on different students to tell parts of the story. Remember the story well, because you're going to write it after we tell it.

- Listen big:

> Ricky read a very long book about a jewel robbery. Somebody stole jewels that were worth more than one million dollars. A policeman tried to find out who the robber was. The book was very exciting. At last Ricky came to the part that told who robbed the jewels, but the last page of the book was missing.
>
> Ricky looked and looked for the missing page but he couldn't find it. So he called his friend Lilly. She had read the book and told him that the jewel robber was the grandmother.

- Listen to the story again:

> Ricky read a very long book about a jewel robbery. Somebody stole jewels that were worth more than one million dollars. A policeman tried to find out who the robber was. The book was very exciting. At last Ricky came to the part that told who robbed the jewels, but the last page of the book was missing.
>
> Ricky looked and looked for the missing page but he couldn't find it. So he called his friend Lilly. She had read the book and told him that the jewel robber was the grandmother.

2. Here's the first sentence of the story: **Ricky read a very long book about a jewel robbery.**

- Everybody, say that sentence. (Signal.) *Ricky read a very long book about a jewel robbery.*

3. Start with the words **somebody stole jewels that were worth . . .** and tell what they were worth and who was trying to find the robber. (Call on different students. Idea: *Somebody stole jewels that were worth one million dollars. A policeman tried to find out who the robber was.*)

- Tell what happened when Ricky came to the part that told who robbed the jewels. (Call on different students. Ideas: *The last page of the book was missing. Ricky looked and looked for the missing page.*)

- Tell what Ricky did to find out who stole the jewels and tell who was the robber. (Call on different students. Ideas: *He called his friend Lilly, who had read the book. She told him that the robber was the grandmother.*)

4. I'll tell the whole story one more time:

> Ricky read a very long book about a jewel robbery. Somebody stole jewels that were worth more than one million dollars. A policeman tried to find out who the robber was. The book was very exciting. At last Ricky came to the part that told who robbed the jewels, but the last page of the book was missing.
>
> Ricky looked and looked for the missing page but he couldn't find it. So he called his friend Lilly. She had read the book and told him that the jewel robber was the grandmother.

5. (Call on different students to tell the whole story. Praise accounts that have most of the detail. For parts that are left out, ask other students:) Who can tell me about an important part that was left out of that story?
6. Everybody, you're going to write the whole story. Write it just the way you heard it. Raise your hand when you're finished.
   (Observe students and give feedback.)
   - (Call on different students to read the whole story. Praise accounts that have most of the detail. For parts that are left out, ask other students:) Who can tell me an important part that was left out of that story?
7. (Collect papers. Mark errors in clarity, spelling and punctuation. During the next language period, pass back the corrected papers and present Exercise B.)

EXERCISE B

REWRITING

- (Return corrected papers to students.)
- You did a good job the first time you wrote about Ricky. Now you're going to write a perfect paper. Rewrite the whole story from the beginning. Write it so it doesn't have any mistakes.
- (After students complete their final draft, post the papers [and illustrations] of the story.)

Extension Lesson 56

Materials: Each student will need lined paper.
Objective A: Reconstruct a dictated passage.
Objective B: Rewrite [and illustrate] the story.

EXERCISE A

RETELLING

1. I'll tell a story twice. Then you'll write the story just the way you'll hear it.
• Listen:

> An old man sat on a rock as he fished. He sat on that rock and fished for hours, but he didn't catch any fish. At last he stood up and said, "I need to find a soft place to sit."
>
> A pig called to him and said, "Come over here and sit. This place is nice and soft."
>
> The old man did that. The place was soft all right. But it was also wet and muddy. The old man was sitting next to a pig in a mudhole. The old man was going to complain, but then he realized that this place felt a lot better than that hard rock.

• Listen to the story again:

> An old man sat on a rock as he fished. He sat on that rock and fished for hours, but he didn't catch any fish. At last he stood up and said, "I need to find a soft place to sit."
>
> A pig called to him and said, "Come over here and sit. This place is nice and soft."
>
> The old man did that. The place was soft all right. But it was also wet and muddy. The old man was sitting next to a pig in a mudhole. The old man was going to complain, but then he realized that this place felt a lot better than that hard rock.

2. Here's the first sentence in the story: **An old man sat on a rock as he fished.**
• Everybody, say that sentence. (Signal.) *An old man sat on a rock as he fished.*
3. Start with that sentence and tell the whole story. (Call on different students to tell the whole story. Praise accounts that have most of the detail. For parts that are left out, ask other students:) Who can tell me about an important part that was left out of that story?
4. Everybody, you're going to write the whole story. Raise your hand when you're finished.
(Observe students and give feedback.)

- (Call on different students to read the whole story. Praise accounts that have most of the detail. For parts that are left out, ask other students:) Who can tell me about an important part that was left out of that story?

5. (Collect papers. Mark errors in clarity, spelling and punctuation. During the next language period, pass back the corrected papers.)

EXERCISE B

REWRITING

- (Return corrected papers to students.)
- You did a good job the first time you wrote about the old man. Now you're going to write a perfect paper. Rewrite the whole story from the beginning. Write it so it doesn't have any mistakes.
- (After students complete their final draft, post the papers [and illustrations] of the story.)

Materials: Each student will need a copy of BLM 57 and lined paper.

Objective A: **Write a report about a specified topic.**

Objective B: Rewrite [and illustrate] the report.

EXERCISE A

TOPICS

BLM 57

Write about a person you admire.

Why I Admire

A person I really admire is

(tell who)

I admire because

(tell why)

One time (tell something the person did that you admire)

Another time (tell something else the person did that you admire)

I hope (tell what you hope about that person)

196

1. (Hand out BLM 57.)
- (Write on the board:)

admire

- You're going to write about somebody you really admire. When you admire people, you think they are great and you would like to be like them. You know somebody who you really admire.
- You're going to write about that person. Remember, it has to be somebody you know, not a movie star or a singer that you really like.

2. Raise your hand if you know who you'd like to write about. ✔
(Call on different students. Ask:)
   - Who do you admire?
   - Why do you admire that person?
   (Praise good reasons.)
   - Can you think of one or two things that person does that show why you admire the person?
3. (Write on the board:)

Why I Admire ________

- Write the title: **Why I Admire . . .** and tell who you admire.
(Observe students and give feedback.)

4. (Write on the board:)

WHO

- Start with the words **a person I really admire is** and tell who that person is. Remember to indent. Raise your hand when you're finished.
(Observe students and give feedback.)
- (Call on different students to read their first sentence: *A person I really admire is* ________.)

5. (Write on the board:)

WHY

- Write one or two sentences that tell what you admire about that person. Do you admire the person's courage or the person's work, or do you admire the things that the person does? Raise your hand when you've written one or two sentences that tell why you admire the person.
  (Observe students and give feedback.)
- (Call on different students to read their sentences. Praise sentences that clearly specify the reasons.)

6. (Write on the board:)

EXAMPLES

- Now you're going to give two examples of something the person did that you really admire. Start with the words **one time** and tell what happened one time. Remember to indent. Raise your hand when you've written that much.
  (Observe students and give feedback.)
- Start the next paragraph with the words **another time** and tell what the person you admire did another time. Raise your hand when you're finished.
  (Observe students and give feedback.)
- (Call on different students to read their examples. Praise good accounts. Offer suggestions for sentences that are vague or that don't provide much detail.)

7. (Write on the board:)

I hope __________.

- Now write your ending. Tell what you hope. Do you hope to be like that person? Do you hope that you'll have the person's courage or strength? What do you hope? Start with the words **I hope** and tell what you hope about that person. Remember to indent.
  (Observe students and give feedback.)
- (Call on different students to read their ending. Praise good accounts.)

8. (Call on different students to read their entire account. Praise parts that are good, and offer suggestions about organization, missing parts and parts that need work.)
9. (Collect papers. Mark errors in spelling and usage.)

EXERCISE B
REWRITING

- (Return papers during the next language period. Students are to write a final draft and possibly make an illustration for their account.)

Extension Lesson 58

Materials: Each student will need a copy of BLM 58 and lined paper.

Objective A: Write a report about a specified topic.

Objective B: Rewrite [and illustrate] the report.

EXERCISE A

TOPICS

BLM 58

Write about jobs you would like.

Jobs I Would Like

When I grow up, I would like to be a ___ or a ___.

Here are the reasons I would like to be a ___.

One reason is ___.

Another reason is ___.

Here are the reasons I would like to be a ___.

One reason is ___.

Another reason is ___.

137

1. (Hand out BLM 58.)
• (Write on the board:)

The Job I Would Like **Jobs I Would Like**

• You're going to write about jobs that you would like to have when you grow up. What would you like to be? Would you like to be a baseball player or a football player, a doctor, a teacher or a truck driver? Maybe you would like to be a writer or an artist. Maybe you would like to be a fire fighter or a police officer. Maybe you want to own a store, or maybe you would like to be a pilot. Maybe you would like to be the mayor of a city, or even the President of the United States.
• You're going to write about jobs you would like to have when you grow up. Figure out how many jobs you're going to tell about. Maybe there is only one that you really like, or maybe there are two or three that you are interested in. Raise your hand if you know one job or two jobs or three jobs that would interest you. ✔
• (Call on different students to tell how many jobs they think they would like and to name those jobs.)

2. Everybody, write the title to your account. If you are interested in one job, write the title: **The Job I Would Like.** If you are interested in two or three jobs, write the title: **Jobs I Would Like.** Raise your hand when you've written your title.
(Observe students and give feedback.)

3. (Write on the board:)

WHAT JOB

• Indent and start with the words **when I grow up, I would like to be a** and name the job or jobs. Raise your hand when you're finished.
(Observe students and give feedback.)

- (Call on different students to read their first sentence: *When I grow up, I would like to be a(n) ________ or a(n) __________.*)

4. (Write on the board:)

WHY

- You're going to write a paragraph that tells two reasons why you would like the first job you listed. If you're writing about being a pilot, start your paragraph with the words: **Here are the reasons I would like to be a pilot.** Write your sentence. Remember to indent. Raise your hand when you've done that much. (Observe students and give feedback.)
- Start your next sentence with the words **one reason is.** Start the following sentence with the words **another reason is.** Raise your hand when you've written two reasons you would like the first job you listed. Raise your hand when you're finished. (Observe students and give feedback.)
- (Call on different students to read their sentences. Praise sentences that clearly specify the reasons.)

5. Now you're going to write a paragraph that tells two reasons you would like the second job you listed. Start your paragraph with the words: **Here are the reasons I would like to be a . . .** and name the job. Then give your reasons. Raise your hand when you're finished. (Observe students and give feedback.)
6. (Repeat step 5 for directing students to write about other jobs students had selected.)
7. (Call on different students to read their entire account. Praise parts that are good, and offer suggestions about organization, missing parts and parts that need work.)
8. (Collect papers. Mark errors in spelling and usage.)

EXERCISE B
REWRITING

- (Return papers during the next language period. Students are to write a final draft and possibly make an illustration for their account.)

Extension Lesson 59

Materials: Each student will need a copy of BLM 59 and lined paper.

Objective A: **Write a multiparagraph story that infers and reports about a picture.**

Objective B: Rewrite [and illustrate] the story.

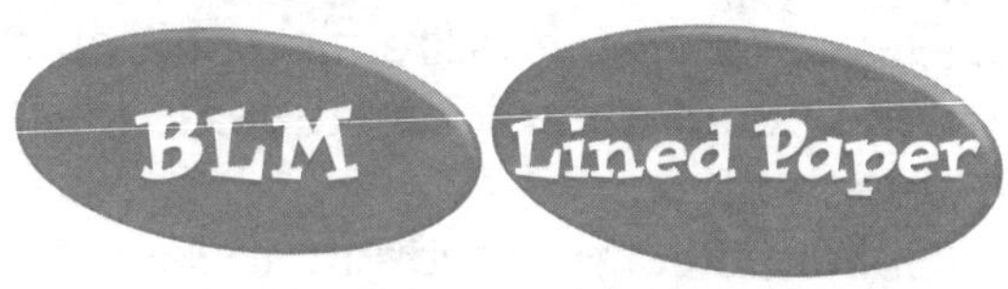

EXERCISE A

PASSAGE WRITING

VAGUE PICTURE

BLM 59

Write an interesting story about this picture.

- Tell what happened before the picture.
- Tell what happened in the picture.
- Tell what happened after the picture.
- You can write as many paragraphs as you want. Make your story interesting.

1. (Hand out BLM 59.)
- You're going to write an interesting story about the picture. You'll tell about what happened **before** the picture, what happened **in** the picture and what happened **after** the picture.
- Remember, first tell what happened before the picture. What do you tell first? (Signal.) *What happened before the picture.*
- What do you tell next? (Signal.) *What happened in the picture.* Yes, what happened in the picture. You'll tell what the woman was thinking, feeling and doing.
- What will you tell last? (Signal.) *What happened after the picture.*

2. You can write as many paragraphs as you want. Make your story interesting. Raise your hand when you're finished. (Observe students and give feedback.)
3. (Call on different students to read their entire passage. Praise good parts. Offer suggestions about organization, missing parts or parts that need work.)
4. (Collect papers. Mark errors in spelling and usage.)

EXERCISE B

REWRITING

- (Return papers during the next language period. Students are to write a final draft and possibly make an illustration for their account.)

Extension Lesson 60

Materials: Each student will need lined paper.
Objective A: Reconstruct a dictated passage.
Objective B: Rewrite [and illustrate] the story.

EXERCISE A

RETELLING

1. I'll tell a story twice. Then you'll write the story just the way you'll hear it.
- Listen:

> An old man left his fishing pole by the rock, and he sat in the mud with a pig. Just then he looked over at the rock and saw that his fishing pole was moving along the ground. "Oh, oh," he said. "I caught a fish."
> He stood up and tried to run, but he fell in the mud. He got up again, and this time he ran to his fishing pole. He pulled the line out of the water. An old tire was on the line.

- Listen to the story again:

> An old man left his fishing pole by the rock, and he sat in the mud with a pig. Just then he looked over at the rock and saw that his fishing pole was moving along the ground. "Oh, oh," he said. "I caught a fish."
> He stood up and tried to run, but he fell in the mud. He got up again, and this time he ran to his fishing pole. He pulled the line out of the water. An old tire was on the line.

2. Here's the first sentence in the story: **An old man left his fishing pole by the rock, and he sat in the mud with a pig.**
- Say that sentence. (Call on different students.) *An old man left his fishing pole by the rock, and he sat in the mud with a pig.*
3. Start with that sentence and tell the whole story. (Call on different students. Praise accounts that have most of the detail. For parts that are left out, ask other students:) Who can tell me about an important part that was left out of that story?
4. Everybody, you're going to write the whole story. Raise your hand when you're finished.
(Observe students and give feedback.)
- (Call on different students to read the whole story. Praise accounts that have most of the detail. For parts that are left out, ask other students:) Who can tell me about an important part that was left out of that story?
5. (Collect papers. Mark errors in clarity, spelling and punctuation.)

EXERCISE B

REWRITING

- (Return corrected papers to students.)
- You did a good job writing about the old man. Now you're going to write a perfect paper. Rewrite the whole story from the beginning. Write it so it doesn't have any mistakes.
- (After students complete their final draft, post the papers [and illustrations] of the story.)

Extension Lesson 61

Materials: Each student will need lined paper.

Objective A: Reconstruct a dictated passage.

Objective B: Rewrite [and illustrate] the story.

EXERCISE A

RETELLING

1. I'll tell a story twice. Then you'll write the story just the way you'll hear it.
- Listen big:

> Fred did not know math, but his horse was good at math. If you asked the horse how many days were in a week, the horse would stamp on the ground 7 times. One day Fred took his horse to the store. Fred wanted to know how much a basketball and a pair of shoes would cost. The horse stamped 75 times. Fred did not have that much money, so he just bought the basketball.

- Listen to the story again:

> Fred did not know math, but his horse was good at math. If you asked the horse how many days were in a week, the horse would stamp on the ground 7 times. One day Fred took his horse to the store. Fred wanted to know how much a basketball and a pair of shoes would cost. The horse stamped 75 times. Fred did not have that much money, so he just bought the basketball.

2. Here's the first sentence in the story: **Fred did not know math, but his horse was good at math.**
- Say that sentence. (Call on different students.) *Fred did not know math, but his horse was good at math.*
3. Start with that sentence and tell the whole story. (Call on different students to tell the whole story. Praise accounts that have most of the detail. For parts that are left out, ask other students:) Who can tell me about an important part that was left out of that story?
4. Everybody, you're going to write the whole story. Raise your hand when you're finished.
(Observe students and give feedback.)
- (Call on different students to read the whole story. Praise accounts that have most of the detail. For parts that are left out, ask other students:) Who can tell me about an important part that was left out of that story?
5. (Collect papers. Mark errors in clarity, spelling and punctuation.)

EXERCISE B

REWRITING

- (Return corrected papers to students.)
- You did a good job the first time you wrote about Fred. Now you're going to write a perfect paper. Rewrite the whole story from the beginning. Write it so it doesn't have any mistakes.
- (After students complete their final draft, post the papers [and illustrations] of the story.)

Extension Lesson 62

Materials: Each student will need a copy of BLM 62, lined paper and illustrating materials.

Objective A: Write a report about a specified topic.

Objective B: Rewrite and illustrate the report.

EXERCISE A

TOPICS

BLM 62

Write about a time you did something that was really good.

Something Really Good

I did something really good (tell when) ____.

I was (tell where) ____.

I was there because (tell why) ____.

(Tell what happened. Tell what you did that was good. Tell all the important things.) ____

Copyright © by SRA/McGraw-Hill. Permission is granted to reproduce this page for classroom use.

1. (Hand out BLM 62.)
- You're going to write about a time you did something that was really **good.** That's something you're really proud you did. First we'll talk about it.

2. (Write on the board:)

WHEN

- Listen: The first thing you'll tell about is when it happened. Was it in the summer or was it in the middle of winter? Do you remember the year it was? Do you remember how old you were?
- Start with the words **I did something really good** and tell when it happened. (Call on different students. Praise students who start with the words *I did something really good* and who give some indication of when.)

  (To correct: If students start to tell more than **when,** stop them and remind them that they are just telling **when.**)

3. (Write on the board:)

WHERE

- The next thing you'll tell is where it happened. Were you at home or somewhere else? Were you in a car or a house, or were you on your bike? Where were you?
- Start with the words **I was** and tell where you were. You can also tell who you were with. (Call on different students. Praise accounts that start with the words *I was* and that tell where the student was and possibly who was with the student.)

4. (Write on the board:)

WHY

- Listen: After you tell about where you were, tell **why** you were there. What were you doing? What did you plan to do?
- Start with the words **I was there because** and tell why you were there. (Call on different students. Praise students who start with the words *I was there because* and who tell the reason.)
  (To correct: If students tell more than **why** they were there, stop them and remind them that they are simply telling **why** they were there.)

5. (Write on the board:)

WHAT HAPPENED

- After you tell why you were at the place, tell what happened. Tell what you did that was good. Tell all the important things that went on. Tell what you did that was good and why you were proud of what you did. If you helped somebody else, tell how that person felt and what that person said. (Call on different students. Praise accounts that give details about what happened.)

6. (Write on the board:)

Something Really Good

- Now you're going to write your report on lined paper. Copy the title on the top line of your paper. Raise your hand when you've done that much.
  (Observe students and give feedback.)

7. First you'll tell when. Start with the words **I did something really good** and tell when it happened. Write one or more sentences. Remember to indent. Raise your hand when you've done that much.
   (Observe students and give feedback.)
8. Now you're going to tell where you were. Start with the words **I was** and tell where you were. If you were with somebody else, you can also tell who was with you. Raise your hand when you've written about where you were.
   (Observe students and give feedback.)
9. Now you're going to tell why you were there. Start with the words **I was there because** and tell why you were there. Tell what you planned to do there. Raise your hand when you're finished.
   (Observe students and give feedback.)
10. Now you're going to write about what you did that was really good. Remember, tell what you did that was really good and tell why it was good. Tell how you felt. If you helped somebody else, tell what that person said. Raise your hand when you're finished.
    (Observe students and give feedback.)
    - Now you can write an ending. You can tell what happened later on. Raise your hand when you're finished.
      (Observe students and give feedback.)
11. (Call on different students to read their entire account. Give feedback about good parts and parts that have problems.)
12. (Collect papers and give feedback for changes. Mark sentences that do not have ending marks. Mark parts that do not tell what they are supposed to tell.)

EXERCISE B
REWRITING

- (Students are later to revise their papers and incorporate the changes you indicated.)
- (After revising their reports, have them illustrate their reports with a picture that shows them doing something good. They may write labels for the people or things in the picture.)

Extension Lesson 63

Materials: Each student will need a copy of BLM 63, lined paper and illustrating materials.

Objective A: Write a report about a specified topic.

Objective B: Rewrite and illustrate the report.

EXERCISE A

TOPICS

BLM 63

Write about something you did that you are sorry about.

Something I Am Sorry About

I did something that I felt really sorry about (tell when) ______.

I was (tell where) ______.

I was there because (tell why) ______.

If I could do it again, I would (tell what you would do) ______.

200

1. (Hand out BLM 63.)
- You're going to write about a time you did something that you really felt sorry about later on.

2. (Write on the board:)

WHEN

- Listen: The first thing you'll tell about is when it happened. Was it in the summer or was it in the middle of winter? Do you remember the year it was? Do you remember how old you were?
- Indent for this sentence. Start with the words **I did something that I felt really sorry about** and tell when it happened. Raise your hand when you've completed your first sentence. (Observe students and give feedback.)
- Read your sentence. (Call on different students. Praise students who start with the words *I did something that I felt really sorry about* and who give some indication of when.)

3. (Write on the board:)

WHERE

- The next sentence you'll write tells where it happened. Were you at home or somewhere else? Were you in a car or a house, or were you on your bike? Where were you when you did something you felt really sorry about?
- Start with the words **I was** and tell where you were. You can also tell who you were with. Raise your hand when you've written the sentence. (Observe students and give feedback.)
- Read your sentence. (Call on different students. Praise accounts that start with the words *I was* and that tell where the student was and possibly who was with the student.)

4. (Write on the board:)

WHY

- Write a sentence that tells **why** you were there. What were you doing? What did you plan to do? Start with the words **I was there because** and tell why you were there. Raise your hand when you've written the sentence.
  (Observe students and give feedback.)
- Read your sentence. (Call on different students. Praise sentences that start with the words *I was there because* and that tell the reason.)

5. (Write on the board:)

WHAT HAPPENED

- Tell what you did that you were sorry about. Tell all the important things that went on. Make sure you write enough sentences to explain what you did. Tell what you did and why you were not proud of what you did.
- Read your sentences that tell what happened. (Call on different students. Praise accounts that give details about what happened.)

6. (Write on the board:)

WHAT I SHOULD HAVE DONE

- Now write the last part of your story. Tell what you should have done. Start with the words **if I could do it again, I would** and tell what you would do. You may need more than one sentence to tell this part. Raise your hand when you've done that much.
  (Observe students and give feedback.)
- Read your sentences that tell what you should have done. (Call on different students. Praise accounts that give details about what the students wished they had done.)

7. (Write on the board:)

Something I Am Sorry About

- Copy the title on the top line of your paper. Raise your hand when you've done that much.
  (Observe students and give feedback.)

8. (Call on different students to read their entire account. Give feedback about good parts and parts that have problems.)
9. (Collect papers and give feedback for changes. Mark sentences that do not have ending marks. Mark parts that do not tell what they are supposed to tell.)

EXERCISE B

REWRITING

- (Students are later to revise their papers and incorporate the changes you indicated.)
- (After revising their reports, have them illustrate their reports with a picture that shows either what they did or what they would have liked to have done. They may write labels for the people or things in the picture.)

Extension Lesson 64

Materials: Each student will need lined paper.
Objective A: Write a report about a specified topic.
Objective B: Rewrite [and illustrate] the report.

EXERCISE A

TOPICS

1. (Write on the board:)

admire

- You're going to write about somebody else you really admire. Maybe you don't admire this person quite as much as the other person you wrote about, but you think this person is great and you would like to be like that person in some ways.

2. Raise your hand if you know who you'd like to write about. ✔
(Call on different students. Ask:)
   - Who do you admire?
   - Why do you admire that person?
   - Can you think of one or two things that person does that show why you admire the person?

3. (Write on the board:)

Why I Admire ________

Write the title: **Why I Admire . . .** and tell who you admire.
(Observe students and give feedback.)

4. (Write on the board:)

WHO

- Start with the words **a person I really admire is . . .** and tell who that person is. Raise your hand when you're finished.
(Observe students and give feedback.)
- (Call on different students to read their first sentence: *A person I really admire is ________.*)

5. (Write on the board:)

WHY

- Write one or two sentences that tell what you admire about that person. Do you admire the person's courage or the person's work, or do you admire the things that the person does? Raise your hand when you've written one or two sentences that tell why you admire the person.
(Observe students and give feedback.)
- (Call on different students to read their sentences. Praise sentences that clearly specify the reasons.)

6. (Write on the board:)

EXAMPLES

- Now you're going to give two examples of something the person did that you really admire. Start with the words **one time** and tell what happened one time. Raise your hand when you've written that much.
(Observe students and give feedback.)
- Start the next sentence with the words **another time** and tell what the person you admire did another time. Raise your hand when you're finished.
(Observe students and give feedback.)

- (Call on different students to read their examples. Praise good accounts. Offer suggestions for sentences that are vague or that don't provide much detail.)

7. (Write on the board:)

I hope _________.

- Now write your ending. Tell what you hope. Do you hope to be like that person? Do you hope that you'll have the person's courage or strength? What do you hope? Start with the words **I hope** and tell what you hope about that person. Remember to indent. Raise your hand when you're finished. (Observe students and give feedback.)
- (Call on different students to read their ending. Praise good accounts.)

8. (Call on different students to read their entire account. Praise good parts.)
9. (Collect papers. Mark errors in spelling and usage.)

EXERCISE B

REWRITING

- (Return papers during the next language period.)
- (Students are to write a final draft and possibly make an illustration for their account.)

Extension Lesson 65

Materials: Each student will need a copy of BLM 65 and lined paper.

Objective A: Write a report about a specified topic.

Objective B: Rewrite [and illustrate] the report.

EXERCISE A

TOPICS

BLM 65

My Best Friend

My best friend is (tell who) ______.
Here are three things I really like about (tell who):

1. One thing I really like about my friend is ______.
2. Another thing I really like about my friend is ______.
3. Another thing I really like about my friend is ______.

I hope (write what you hope about yourself and this person) ______.

201

1. (Hand out BLM 65.)
- (Write on the board:)

My Best Friend

- You're going to write about your best friend and tell why you like that person.
- Raise your hand if you know who you'd like to write about. ✔
  (Call on different students. Ask:) Who are you going to write about?

2. The title is: **My Best Friend.** Write the title.
   (Observe students and give feedback.)
3. (Write on the board:)

WHO

- Write a sentence that tells who your best friend is. Raise your hand when you're finished.
  (Observe students and give feedback.)
- (Call on different students to read their first sentence.)

4. (Write on the board:)

WHY
1.
2.
3.

- You're going to make a list of three things you like about the person. Start with the words **here are the three things I really like about . . .** and name the person. Raise your hand when you've written that sentence.
  (Observe students and give feedback.)
- (Call on different students to read their sentence.)

5. On the next line write number 1 and a period. Then write a sentence that tells one thing you like. Maybe it's something you like to do together. Maybe this person makes you laugh a lot, or maybe you like to talk to this person about things that are going on in your life. Start with the words **one thing I really like about my friend.** Raise your hand when you've written your sentence for number 1. Remember, just tell about one thing you like.
   (Observe students and give feedback.)
   - (Call on students to read what they've written for number 1.)
6. Now write number 2 and a period on the next line. On that line, write your sentence for number 2. Raise your hand when you're finished.
   (Observe students and give feedback.)
   - (Call on students to read their sentence for number 2.)
7. Now write number 3 and a period on the next line. On that line, write your sentence for number 3. Raise your hand when you're finished.
   (Observe students and give feedback.)
   - (Call on students to read their sentence for number 3.)
8. (Write on the board:)

   I hope ________.

   - Now write your ending. Tell what you hope. Do you hope that you'll be friends with this person for a long time? Do you hope you'll be able to see this person a lot during the next year? Write what you hope. Raise your hand when you're finished.
   (Observe students and give feedback.)
9. (Call on different students to read their entire account. Praise good parts.)
10. (Collect papers. Mark mistakes in spelling and usage.)

EXERCISE B

REWRITING

- (Return papers during the next language period.)
- (Students are to write a final draft and possibly make an illustration for their account.)

Extension Lesson 66

Materials: Each student will need a copy of BLM 66 and lined paper.

Objective A: Write a multiparagraph story that infers and reports about a picture.

Objective B: Rewrite [and illustrate] the story.

EXERCISE A

PASSAGE WRITING

VAGUE PICTURE

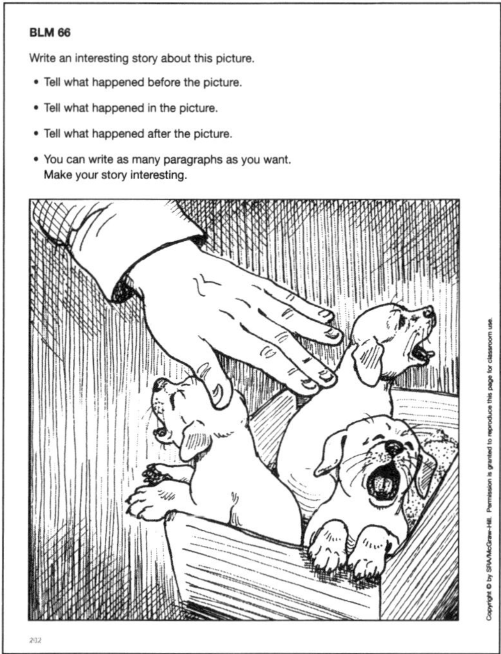
BLM 66

Write an interesting story about this picture.

- Tell what happened before the picture.
- Tell what happened in the picture.
- Tell what happened after the picture.
- You can write as many paragraphs as you want. Make your story interesting.

Copyright © by SRA/McGraw-Hill. Permission is granted to reproduce this page for classroom use.

202

1. (Hand out BLM 66.)
   - You're going to write an interesting story about the picture. You'll tell about what happened before the picture, what happened in the picture and what happened after the picture.
   - Remember, first tell what happened before the picture. What do you tell first? (Signal.) *What happened before the picture.*
   - What do you tell next? (Signal.) *What happened in the picture.* Yes, what happened in the picture. You'll tell what the puppies were thinking, feeling and doing. Tell about the person whose hand is shown.
   - What will you tell last? (Signal.) *What happened after the picture.*
2. You can write as many paragraphs as you want. Make your story interesting. Raise your hand when you're finished. (Observe students and give feedback.)
3. (Call on different students to read their entire passage. Praise good parts. Offer suggestions about organization, missing parts or parts that need work.)
4. (Collect papers. Mark mistakes in spelling and usage.)

EXERCISE B

REWRITING

- (Return papers during the next language period. Students are to write a final draft and possibly make an illustration for their account.)

Extension Lesson 67

Materials: Each student will need lined paper and illustrating materials.

Objective A: Write a report about a specified topic.

Objective B: Rewrite and illustrate the report.

Lined Paper

EXERCISE A

TOPICS

1. You're going to write about a time you did something that was really hard for you to do. Maybe it was something in school that you had trouble learning or doing. Maybe it was something like learning to ride a bike or learning to skateboard.
2. First we'll talk about it.
- (Write on the board:)

WHEN

- Listen: The first thing you'll tell about is **when** it happened. Do you remember the year it was? Do you remember how old you were?
- Start with the words **I did something that was really hard for me to do** and tell when it happened. (Call on different students. Praise students who start with the words *I did something really hard for me to do* and who give some indication of when.)

  (To correct: If students start to tell more than **when,** stop them and remind them that they are just telling **when.**)

3. (Write on the board:)

WHERE

- The next thing you'll tell is where it happened. Start with the words **I was** and tell where you were. You can also tell who you were with. (Call on different students. Praise accounts that start with the words **I was** and that tell where the student was and possibly who was with the student.)

4. (Write on the board:)

WHAT

- The next thing you'll tell is what was really hard for you to do. (Call on different students. Praise accounts that tell what was hard for the students.)

5. (Write on the board:)

WHAT HAPPENED

- Now you'll tell what happened. Tell all the important things that went on. Tell why it was important for you to do it. Tell how you did it and how you felt. (Call on different students. Praise accounts that give details about what happened.)

6. (Write on the board:)

Something That Was Hard for Me

- Now you're going to write your report on lined paper. Copy the title on the top line of your paper. Raise your hand when you've done that much. (Observe students and give feedback.)

7. Now you'll tell when. Start with the words **I did something that was hard for me to do** and tell when it happened. Write one or more sentences. Remember to indent your first sentence. Raise your hand when you've written about when it happened.
   (Observe students and give feedback.)
8. Now you're going to tell where you were. Start with the words **I was** and tell where you were. If you were with somebody else, you can also tell that they were with you. Raise your hand when you've written about where you were.
   (Observe students and give feedback.)
9. Now you're going to tell what happened. Remember, tell about the problems you had and why you wanted to succeed. Tell what you did to succeed. Tell how you felt. Raise your hand when you're finished.
   (Observe students and give feedback.)
10. Now you can write an ending. You can tell what happened later on. Raise your hand when you're finished.
    (Observe students and give feedback.)
11. (Call on different students to read their entire account. Give feedback about good parts and parts that have problems.)
12. (Collect papers and give feedback for changes. Mark sentences that do not have ending marks. Mark parts that do not tell what they are supposed to tell.)

EXERCISE B
REWRITING

- (Students are later to revise their papers and incorporate the changes you indicated.)
- (After revising their reports, have them illustrate their reports with a picture that shows them doing what had been hard for them. They may write labels for the people or things in the picture.)

Extension Lesson 68

Materials: Each student will need lined paper.

Objective A: Reconstruct a dictated passage.

Objective B: Rewrite [and illustrate] the story.

EXERCISE A

RETELLING

1. I'll tell a story twice. Then you'll write the story just the way you'll hear it.
- Listen:

> Jill hated to rake leaves. So one Saturday she decided to talk her little sister into raking the leaves. She told her sister that she could keep anything she found while raking the leaves. She lied and told her little sister, "I always find some money when I rake the leaves. . . ."
>
> So Jill went over to her friend Julie's house and played all afternoon. When she got home, her little sister gave her a big hug and said, "Oh, thank you."
>
> "Why are you thanking me?" Jill asked.
>
> "Because I found 20 dollars when I raked the leaves."
>
> That was the last time Jill didn't rake leaves on Saturday.

- Listen to the story again:

> Jill hated to rake leaves. So one Saturday she decided to talk her little sister into raking the leaves. She told her sister that she could keep anything she found while raking the leaves. She lied and told her little sister, "I always find some money when I rake the leaves. . . ."
>
> So Jill went over to her friend Julie's house and played all afternoon. When she got home, her little sister gave her a big hug and said, "Oh, thank you."
>
> "Why are you thanking me?" Jill asked.
>
> "Because I found 20 dollars when I raked the leaves."
>
> That was the last time Jill didn't rake leaves on Saturday.

2. Here's the first sentence in the story: **Jill hated to rake leaves.**
- Everybody, say that sentence. (Signal.) *Jill hated to rake leaves.*
3. Start with that sentence and tell the whole story. (Call on different students to tell the whole story. Praise accounts that have most of the detail. For parts that are left out, ask other students:) Who can tell me about an important part that was left out of that story?

4. Everybody, you're going to write the whole story. Raise your hand when you're finished.
   (Observe students and give feedback.)
- (Call on different students to read the whole story. Praise accounts that have most of the detail. For parts that are left out, ask other students:) Who can tell me about an important part that was left out of that story?

5. (Collect papers. Mark errors in clarity, spelling and punctuation.)

EXERCISE B

REWRITING

- (Return corrected papers to students.)
- You did a good job the first time you wrote about Jill. Now you're going to write a perfect paper. Rewrite the whole story from the beginning. Write it so it doesn't have any mistakes.
- (After students complete their final draft, post the papers [and illustrations] of the story.)

Extension Lesson 69

Materials: Each student will need lined paper and illustrating materials.
Objective A: Write a report about a specified topic.
Objective B: Rewrite and illustrate their report.

EXERCISE A

TOPICS

1. You're going to write about a time you were really proud of yourself.
- (Write on the board:)

WHEN

2. Listen: The first thing you'll tell about is **when** it happened. Do you remember the year it was? Do you remember how old you were?
- Indent for this sentence. Start with the words **I was really proud of myself . . .** and tell when it happened. Raise your hand when you've completed your first sentence.
(Observe students and give feedback.)
- Read your sentence. (Call on different students. Praise students who start with the words *I was really proud of myself* and who give some indication of when.)

3. (Write on the board:)

WHERE

- The next sentence you'll write tells where it happened. Were you at home or somewhere else? Were you in a car or a house, or were you on your bike? Where were you when something happened that made you really proud of yourself?
- Start with the words **I was** and tell where you were. You can also tell who you were with. Raise your hand when you've written the sentence.
(Observe students and give feedback.)
- Read your sentence. (Call on different students. Praise sentences that start with the words *I was* and that tell where the student was and possibly who was with the student.)

4. (Write on the board:)

WHY

- Write a sentence that tells why you were there. What were you doing? What did you plan to do?
- Start with the words **I was there because** and tell why you were there. Raise your hand when you're finished.
(Observe students and give feedback.)
- Read your sentence. (Call on different students. Praise sentences that start with the words *I was there because* and that tell the reason.)

5. (Write on the board:)

WHAT HAPPENED

- Tell what you did that made you proud of yourself. Make sure you write enough sentences to explain what happened that made you proud. Tell all the important things that went on. Raise your hand when you're finished.
(Observe students and give feedback.)
- (Call on different students. Praise accounts that give details about what happened.)

6. (Write on the board:)

LATER

- Now write the last part of your story. Tell what happened later on. Do you still feel proud? Do you ever think about that time? Does it make you feel good to think about that time?
- Start with the words **later on** and tell what happened later on or how you feel now. You may need more than one sentence to tell this part. Raise your hand when you're finished.
  (Observe students and give feedback.)
- (Call on different students to read their account. Praise accounts that give details about what the students did later on.)

7. (Write on the board:)

Proud of Myself

- Copy the title on the top line of your paper. Raise your hand when you're finished. ✔

8. (Call on different students to read their entire account. Give feedback about good parts and parts that have problems.)
9. (Collect papers and give feedback for changes. Mark sentences that do not have ending marks. Mark parts that do not tell what they are supposed to tell.)

EXERCISE B
REWRITING

- (Students are later to revise their papers and incorporate the changes you indicated.)
- (After students revise their reports, direct students to illustrate their reports with a picture that shows what happened. They may write labels for the people or things in the picture.)

Extension Lesson 70

Materials: Each student will need lined paper.

Objective A: Reconstruct a dictated passage.

Objective B: Rewrite [and illustrate] the story.

EXERCISE A

RETELLING

1. I'll tell a story twice. Then you'll write the story just the way you'll hear it.
- Listen:

> Rita loved to read. But she had already read every book in her house and every book in the library. The bookstore was the only place that had books she hadn't read. So she got a job in the bookstore. When the store was busy, Rita worked. When she had free time, she read.

- Listen to the story again:

> Rita loved to read. But she had already read every book in her house and every book in the library. The bookstore was the only place that had books she hadn't read. So she got a job in the bookstore. When the store was busy, Rita worked. When she had free time, she read.

2. Here's the first sentence in the story: **Rita loved to read.**
- Everybody, say that sentence. (Signal.) *Rita loved to read.*

3. Start with that sentence and tell the whole story. (Call on different students to tell the whole story. Praise accounts that have most of the detail. For parts that are left out, ask other students:) Who can tell me about an important part that was left out of that story?
4. Everybody, you're going to write the whole story. Raise your hand when you're finished.
(Observe students and give feedback.)
- (Call on different students to read the whole story. Praise accounts that have most of the detail. For parts that are left out, ask other students:) Who can tell me about an important part that was left out of that story?

5. (Collect papers. Mark errors in clarity, spelling and punctuation.)

EXERCISE B

REWRITING

- (Return corrected papers to students.)
- You did a good job the first time you wrote about Rita. Now you're going to write a perfect paper. Rewrite the whole story from the beginning. Write it so it doesn't have any mistakes.
- (After students complete their final draft, post the papers [and illustrations] of the story.)

Extension Lesson 71

Materials: Each student will need a copy of BLM 71 and lined paper.

Objective A: Write a report about a specified topic.

Objective B: Rewrite [and illustrate] the report.

EXERCISE A

TOPICS

BLM 71

What I Worked On in School Yesterday

Here are the subjects I worked on yesterday: (tell subjects)

Here are some of the things we did during reading. (Tell about two or more things that happened during reading.)

Here are some of the things we did during math. (Tell about two or more things that happened during math.)

Here are some of the things we did during (name another subject) (Tell about two or more things that happened during that subject.)

203

1. (Hand out BLM 71.)

- (Write on the board:)

What I Worked On in School Yesterday

- You're going to write about what you did in school yesterday. Everybody, copy the title.
(Observe students and give feedback.)

2. You have to organize how you'll tell about what you did. Here's one way: You could tell about what you did in each subject. What subjects did you work on in school yesterday? (Call on several students. Ideas: *Reading, math, language, writing,* etc.)
3. First you'll start with a sentence that names all the subjects that you worked on yesterday. Start with the words **here are the subjects I worked on yesterday.** Then just list the subjects. Raise your hand when you're finished.
(Observe students and give feedback.)

- (Call on different students to read their sentences. Idea: *Here are the subjects I worked on yesterday: reading, math, language, writing.*)

4. Now you'll write a paragraph that tells what you did in reading. Begin with a sentence that says: **Here are some of the things we did during reading.** Then list two or more things that happened during reading. Raise your hand when you're finished.
(Observe students and give feedback.)

- (Call on different students to read their sentences. Praise paragraphs that tell about two or three things studied in reading.)

5. Now write a paragraph that tells what you did in math. Begin your paragraph with a sentence that says: **Here are some of the things we did during math.** Then list two or more things that happened during math. Raise your hand when you're finished.
   (Observe students and give feedback.)
   - (Call on different students to read their paragraph.)
6. Now write a paragraph that tells what you did in another subject. Begin your paragraph with a sentence that says: **Here are some of the things we did during . . .** and name the subject. Then write about two or more things that happened during that subject. Raise your hand when you're finished.
   (Observe students and give feedback.)
   - (Call on different students to read their paragraph.)
7. (Call on different students to read their entire account. Give feedback about good parts and about problems.)
8. (Collect papers. Mark mistakes in spelling and usage.)

EXERCISE B

REWRITING

- (Return papers during the next language period.)
- (Students are to write a final draft and possibly make an illustration for their account.)

Extension Lesson 72

Materials: Each student will need lined paper.
Objective A: Reconstruct a dictated passage.
Objective B: Rewrite [and illustrate] the story.

EXERCISE A
RETELLING

1. I'll tell a story twice. Then you'll write the story just the way you'll hear it.
- Listen:

> Rose had three dollars. She wanted to buy a stuffed animal, but stuffed animals cost four dollars. Her friend Pam said, "If I put up two dollars and you put up two dollars, we'll have four dollars for a stuffed animal." So the girls went into the store.
>
> Pam gave the clerk two dollars, and Rose gave the clerk two dollars. Then Rose told the clerk, "We gave you four dollars. Please give us a stuffed animal."
>
> The clerk gave the girls a stuffed animal.

- Listen to the story again:

> Rose had three dollars. She wanted to buy a stuffed animal, but stuffed animals cost four dollars. Her friend Pam said, "If I put up two dollars and you put up two dollars, we'll have four dollars for a stuffed animal." So the girls went into the store.
>
> Pam gave the clerk two dollars, and Rose gave the clerk two dollars. Then Rose told the clerk, "We gave you four dollars. Please give us a stuffed animal."
>
> The clerk gave the girls a stuffed animal.

2. Here's the first sentence in the story: **Rose had three dollars.**
- Everybody, say that sentence. (Signal.) *Rose had three dollars.*
3. Start with that sentence and tell the whole story. (Call on different students to tell the whole story. Praise accounts that have most of the detail. For parts that are left out, ask other students:) Who can tell me about an important part that was left out of that story?

4. Everybody, you're going to write the whole story. Raise your hand when you're finished.
   (Observe students and give feedback.)
   - (Call on different students to read the whole story. Praise accounts that have most of the detail. For parts that are left out, ask other students:) Who can tell me about an important part that was left out of that story?
5. (Collect papers. Mark errors in clarity, spelling and punctuation.)

EXERCISE B

REWRITING

- (Return corrected papers to students.)
- You did a good job the first time you wrote about Rose. Now you're going to write a perfect paper. Rewrite the whole story from the beginning. Write it so it doesn't have any mistakes.
- (After students complete their final draft, post the papers [and illustrations] of the story.)

Extension Lesson 73

Materials: Each student will need a copy of BLM 73 and lined paper.

Objective A: Write a report about a specified topic.

Objective B: Rewrite [and illustrate] the report.

EXERCISE A

TOPICS

BLM 73

Someone I Would Like to Know Better

One reason I would like to know (name of person) better is (tell reason).

Another reason I would like to know (name of person) better is (tell reason).

A third reason I would like to know (name of person) better is (tell reason).

I hope (write your ending). (Tell what you hope and what you will do.)

204

1. (Hand out BLM 73.)
- (Write on the board:)

Someone I Would Like to Know Better

- You're going to write about someone who you would like to know better. Maybe it is a movie star or somebody in sports. Maybe it is someone you have seen around the school, like a janitor or the principal, who you would like to know better.
- You're going to name the person and give some reasons you would like to know that person better. You should tell what you find interesting about that person and what you would like to find out about that person.
- Write your account. Raise your hand when you're finished.
  (Observe students and give feedback.)

2. (Call on different students to read their entire account. Praise parts that are good, and offer suggestions about organization, missing parts or parts that need work.)
3. (Collect papers. Mark mistakes in spelling and usage.)

EXERCISE B

REWRITING

- (Return papers during the next language period.)
- (Students are to write a final draft and possibly make an illustration for their account.)

Extension Lesson 74

Materials: Each student will need a copy of BLM 74 and lined paper.

Objective A: Write a multiparagraph story that infers and reports about a picture.

Objective B: Rewrite [and illustrate] the story.

EXERCISE A

PASSAGE WRITING

VAGUE PICTURE

BLM 74

Write an interesting story about this picture.

- Tell what happened before the picture.
- Tell what happened in the picture.
- Tell what happened after the picture.
- You can write as many paragraphs as you want. Make your story interesting.

1. (Hand out BLM 74.)
- You're going to write an interesting story about the picture. You'll tell about what happened before the picture, what happened in the picture and what happened after the picture.
- Remember, first tell what happened before the picture. What do you tell first? (Signal.) *What happened before the picture.*
- What do you tell next? (Signal.) *What happened in the picture.*
  Yes, what happened in the picture. You'll tell what the small girl was thinking, feeling and doing.
- What will you tell last? (Signal.) *What happened after the picture.*

2. You can write as many paragraphs as you want. Make your story interesting. Raise your hand when you're finished. (Observe students and give feedback.)
3. (Call on different students to read their entire passage. Praise good parts. Offer suggestions about organization, missing parts or parts that need work.)
4. (Collect papers. Mark mistakes in spelling and usage.)

EXERCISE B

REWRITING

- (Return papers during the next language period. Students are to write a final draft and possibly make an illustration for their account.)

Extension Lesson 75

Materials: Each student will need lined paper.

Objective A: **Reconstruct a story and write an ending.**

Objective B: Rewrite [and illustrate] the story.

EXERCISE A

PASSAGE WRITING

ENDINGS

1. I'll tell the first part of a story. Then you'll write the part I tell and the ending to the story.
- Listen carefully so that you can tell the story the same way I tell it:

> A dog and a cat were friends. One day, the dog and the cat were walking along when the cat fell into a deep hole. The cat could not get out of the hole. The dog barked and scratched around, but it did not know how to get the cat out of the hole.

- Listen to that part again:

> A dog and a cat were friends. One day, the dog and the cat were walking along when the cat fell into a deep hole. The cat could not get out of the hole. The dog barked and scratched around, but it did not know how to get the cat out of the hole.

2. Here's the first sentence in the story: **A dog and a cat were friends.**
- Everybody, say that sentence. (Signal.) *A dog and a cat were friends.*
- Listen: One day the dog and the cat were doing something when something happened. Start with the words **one day** and say the sentence from the story. (Call on a student. Praise close approximations: *One day, the dog and the cat were walking along when the cat fell into a deep hole.*)

3. (Call on different students to retell the entire first part. Praise accounts that have most of the detail. For parts that are left out, ask other students:) Who can tell me about an important part that was left out of the story?
4. Everybody, you're going to write the whole story. Start out by writing the first part just the way you heard it. Raise your hand when you've done that much. (Observe students and give feedback.)
- (Call on different students to read the first part. Praise and correct.)

5. Now you're going to write an ending that tells how the dog helped the cat get out of the hole. Maybe the dog got someone to help. Maybe the dog figured out what to drop into the hole.
- Everybody, write your ending. Raise your hand when you're finished. (Observe students and give feedback.)

6. (Call on different students to read their ending. Praise good plans.)
7. (Collect papers. Mark errors in clarity, spelling and punctuation.)

EXERCISE B

REWRITING

- (Return papers during the next language period.)
- You did a good job the first time you wrote about the dog and the cat. Now you're going to write a perfect paper. Rewrite the whole story from the beginning. Write it so it doesn't have any mistakes.
- (After students complete their final draft, post the papers [and illustrations] of the story.)

Extension Lesson 76

Materials: Each student will need lined paper and illustrating materials.

Objective A: Write a report about a specified topic.

Objective B: Rewrite and illustrate their report.

EXERCISE A

TOPICS

1. You're going to write about a time you helped somebody.
2. (Write on the board:)

WHEN

- Listen: The first thing you'll tell about is when it happened.
- Start with the words **I helped somebody** and tell when it happened. Raise your hand when you've completed your first sentence.
  (Observe students and give feedback.)
- (Call on different students to read their sentence. Praise students who start with the words *I helped somebody* and who give some indication of when.)

3. (Write on the board:)

WHERE

- The next sentence you'll write tells where it happened. Were you at home or somewhere else? Were you in a car or a house, or were you on your bike? Where were you when you helped somebody?
- Start with the words **I was** and tell where you were. You can also tell who you were with. Raise your hand when you've written the sentence.
  (Observe students and give feedback.)
- (Call on different students to read their sentence. Praise sentences that start with the words *I was* and that tell where the student was and possibly who was with the student.)

4. (Write on the board:)

WHO
WHY

- Write a sentence that tells who needed help and why that person needed help. Start with the name of the person and tell why the person needed help. Tell the problem the person had. Raise your hand when you're finished.
  (Observe students and give feedback.)
- (Call on different students to read their sentence. Praise sentences that start with the person's name and tell the problem the person had.)

5. (Write on the board:)

WHAT HAPPENED

- Tell what you did to help the person. Tell all the important things that happened. Raise your hand when you've finished telling about what happened.
  (Observe students and give feedback.)
- (Call on different students to read their account. Praise accounts that give details about what happened.)

6. (Write on the board:)

LATER

- Now write the last part of your story. Tell what happened later on. Did the person thank you? Was the person grateful because of what you did? Are you glad that you did what you did?
- Start with the words **later on** and tell what happened later on or how you felt later on. You may need more than one sentence to tell this part. Raise your hand when you're finished.
  (Observe students and give feedback.)
- (Call on different students to read their account.)

7. (Write on the board:)

Proud of Myself

- Copy the title on the top line of your paper. Raise your hand when you're finished.
  (Observe students and give feedback.)

8. (Call on different students to read their entire account. Give feedback about good parts and parts that have problems.)
9. (Collect papers and give feedback for changes. Mark sentences that do not have ending marks. Mark parts that do not tell what they are supposed to tell.)

EXERCISE B
REWRITING

- (Students are later to revise their papers and incorporate the changes you indicated.)
- (After students revise their reports, direct students to illustrate their reports with a picture that shows what happened. They may write labels for the people or things in the picture.)

Extension Lesson 77

Materials: Each student will need lined paper.

Objective A: Reconstruct a story and write an ending.

Objective B: Rewrite [and illustrate] the story.

EXERCISE A

PASSAGE WRITING

ENDINGS

1. I'll tell the first part of a story. Then you'll write that part and write a good ending to the story.
- Listen big:

> A dog named Fluffy told her mom, "I'm going fishing."
> The mom said, "But you don't have a fishing pole."
> Fluffy said, "I'll just tie the fishing line to my tail."
> That's what the dog did. She went to the lake, tied the line around her tail and sat down.

2. Here's the first sentence in the story: **A dog named Fluffy told her mom, "I'm going fishing."**
- Everybody, say that sentence. (Signal.) *A dog named Fluffy told her mom, "I'm going fishing."*

3. I'll tell the whole story one more time. Then you'll tell the first part. You'll start with the words: **A dog named Fluffy told her mom, "I'm going fishing."**
- Listen:

> A dog named Fluffy told her mom, "I'm going fishing."
> The mom said, "But you don't have a fishing pole."
> Fluffy said, "I'll just tie the fishing line to my tail."
> That's what the dog did. She went to the lake, tied the line around her tail and sat down.

4. (Call on different students to retell the entire first part. Praise accounts that have most of the detail. For parts that are left out, ask other students:) Who can tell me about an important part that was left out of the story?
5. Everybody, you're going to write the whole story. Start out by writing the first part just the way you heard it. Raise your hand when you've done that much. (Observe students and give feedback.)
- (Call on different students to read the first part. Praise and correct.)

6. Now you're going to write an ending that tells what happened when Fluffy went fishing. Maybe she caught a fish. Maybe she caught something that wasn't a fish.
- Everybody, write your ending. Raise your hand when you're finished. (Observe students and give feedback.)
- (Call on different students to read their whole story. Praise good endings. Praise accounts that have most of the detail.)

7. (Collect papers. Mark errors in clarity, spelling and punctuation.)

EXERCISE B

REWRITING

- (Return papers during the next language period.)
- You did a good job the first time you wrote about Fluffy. Now you're going to write a perfect paper. Rewrite the whole story from the beginning. Write it so it doesn't have any mistakes.
- (After students complete their final draft, post the papers [and illustrations] of the story.)

Extension Lesson 78

Materials: Each student will need lined paper.

Objective A: Write a report about a specified topic.

Objective B: Rewrite [and illustrate] their report.

EXERCISE A

TOPICS

1. You're going to write about what you worked on in school yesterday. You'll use the same organization that you used before, but I won't go over it with you first.

- Write an account that has a title. Tell about the things you worked on in school yesterday. Remember to name the subjects and tell about the things you did for each subject. Raise your hand when you're finished.
  (Observe students and give feedback.)

2. (Call on different students to read their entire account. Give feedback about good parts and parts that have problems.)
3. (Collect papers. Mark mistakes in spelling and usage.)

EXERCISE B

REWRITING

- (Return papers during the next language period.)
- (Students are to write a final draft and possibly make an illustration for their account.)

Extension Lesson 79

Materials: Each student will need lined paper.

Objective A: Reconstruct a story and write an ending.

Objective B: Rewrite [and illustrate] the story.

EXERCISE A

PASSAGE WRITING

ENDINGS

1. I'll tell the first part of a story. Then you'll write that part and write a good ending to the story.
- Listen big:

> There once was a plane named Herbie that got tired of flying. He told his brother, "From now on, I'm going to go on roads, just like a car." Herbie tried going down a road, but it didn't work well. Herbie's wings stuck out too far and the cars kept running into Herbie's wings.

2. Here's the first sentence in the story: **There once was a plane named Herbie that got tired of flying.**
- Everybody, say that sentence. (Signal.) *There once was a plane named Herbie that got tired of flying.*
- Did Herbie like to fly anymore? (Signal.) *No.*
3. I'll tell the whole story one more time. Then you'll tell the first part. You'll start with the words: **There once was a plane named Herbie that got tired of flying.**
- Listen:

> There once was a plane named Herbie that got tired of flying. He told his brother, "From now on, I'm going to go on roads, just like a car." Herbie tried going down a road, but it didn't work well. Herbie's wings stuck out too far and the cars kept running into Herbie's wings.

4. (Call on different students to retell the entire first part. Praise accounts that have most of the detail. For parts that are left out, ask other students:) Who can tell me about an important part that was left out of the story?
5. Everybody, you're going to write the whole story. Start out by writing the first part just the way you heard it. Raise your hand when you've done that much. (Observe students and give feedback.)
- (Call on different students to read the first part. Praise and correct.)
6. Now you're going to write an ending that tells how Herbie solved the problem. Maybe he did something with his wings. Maybe he figured out where he could go where his wings would not get in the way. Maybe he changed his mind about flying.
- Everybody, write your ending. Raise your hand when you're finished. (Observe students and give feedback.)
- (Call on different students to read their whole story. Praise good endings. Praise accounts that have most of the detail.)

7. (Collect papers. Mark errors in clarity, spelling and punctuation.)

EXERCISE B
REWRITING

- (Return papers during the next language period.)
- You did a good job the first time you wrote about Herbie. Now you're going to write a perfect paper. Rewrite the whole story from the beginning. Write it so it doesn't have any mistakes.
- (After students complete their final draft, post the papers [and illustrations] of the story.)

Extension Lesson 80

Materials: Each student will need a copy of BLM 80 and lined paper.

Objective A: Write a multiparagraph story that infers and reports about a picture.

Objective B: Rewrite [and illustrate] the story.

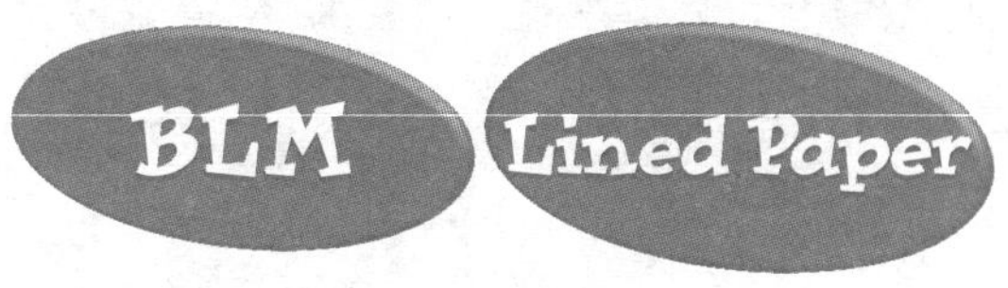

EXERCISE A

PASSAGE WRITING

VAGUE PICTURE

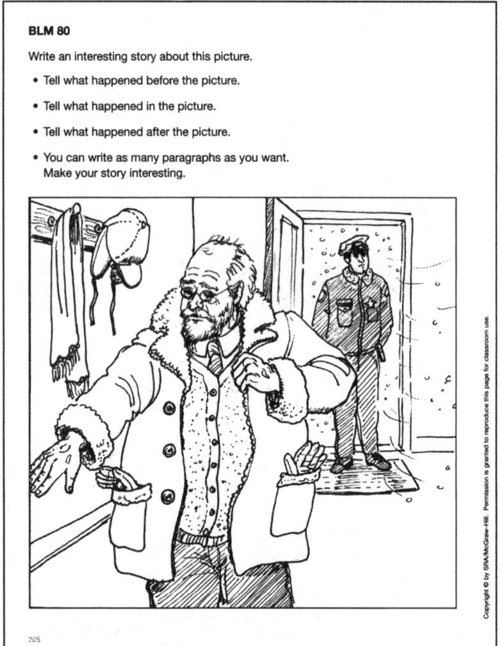

BLM 80

Write an interesting story about this picture.

- Tell what happened before the picture.
- Tell what happened in the picture.
- Tell what happened after the picture.
- You can write as many paragraphs as you want. Make your story interesting.

205

1. (Hand out BLM 80.)
   - You're going to write an interesting story about the picture. You'll tell about what happened before the picture, what happened in the picture and what happened after the picture.
   - Remember, first tell what happened before the picture. What do you tell first? (Signal.) *What happened before the picture.*
   - What do you tell next? (Signal.) *What happened in the picture.* Yes, what happened in the picture. You'll tell what the older man was thinking, feeling and doing.
   - What will you tell last? (Signal.) *What happened after the picture.*
2. You can write as many paragraphs as you want. Make your story interesting. Raise your hand when you're finished. (Observe students and give feedback.)
3. (Call on different students to read their entire passage. Praise good parts. Offer suggestions about organization, missing parts or parts that need work.)
4. (Collect papers. Mark mistakes in spelling and usage.)

EXERCISE B

REWRITING

- (Return papers during the next language period. Students are to write a final draft and possibly make an illustration for their account.)

Extension Lesson 81

Materials: Each student will need lined paper.

Objective A: Write a report about a specified topic.

Objective B: Rewrite [and illustrate] their report.

EXERCISE A

TOPICS

1. (Write on the board:)

Someone I Really Admire

- Here's the title for your story.
- Earlier, you wrote about people who you admire. This time, you're going to do it without any help about the kind of sentences to write. You can write about one of the same people you wrote about earlier. Try to make your paper well organized and give good reasons you admire this person. Make your paper interesting to read.
- Write your account. Raise your hand when you're finished.
  (Observe students and give feedback.)

2. (Call on different students to read their entire account. Praise parts that are good, and offer suggestions about organization, missing parts or parts that need work.)
3. (Collect papers. Mark mistakes in spelling and usage.)

EXERCISE B

REWRITING

- (Return papers during the next language period.)
- (Students are to write a final draft and possibly make an illustration for their account.)

Extension Lesson 82

Materials: Each student will need lined paper.

Objective A: Reconstruct a story and write an ending.

Objective B: Rewrite [and illustrate] the story.

EXERCISE A

PASSAGE WRITING

ENDINGS

1. I'll tell the first part of a story. Then you'll write that part and write a good ending to the story.
- Listen:

> Tom went to Hilda's birthday party. After he got there, he realized that he didn't have a gift for Hilda. At first he didn't know what to do. But then he got an idea. He told Hilda, "I have a surprise gift for you."

2. Here's the first sentence in the story: **Tom went to Hilda's birthday party.**
- Everybody, say that sentence. (Signal.) *Tom went to Hilda's birthday party.*
3. I'll tell the whole story one more time. Then you'll tell the first part. You'll start with the words: **Tom went to Hilda's birthday party.**
- Listen:

> Tom went to Hilda's birthday party. After he got there, he realized that he didn't have a gift for Hilda. At first he didn't know what to do. But then he got an idea. He told Hilda, "I have a surprise gift for you."

4. (Call on different students to retell the entire first part. Praise accounts that have most of the detail. For parts that are left out, ask other students:) Who can tell me about an important part that was left out of the story?
5. Everybody, you're going to write the whole story. Start out by writing the first part just the way you heard it. Raise your hand when you've done that much. (Observe students and give feedback.)
- (Call on different students to read the first part. Praise and correct.)
6. Now you're going to write an ending that tells about the present Tom had for Hilda.
- Everybody, write your ending. Raise your hand when you're finished. (Observe students and give feedback.)
- (Call on different students to read their whole story. Praise good endings. Praise accounts that have most of the detail.)
7. (Collect papers. Mark errors in clarity, spelling and punctuation.)

EXERCISE B

REWRITING

- (Return papers during the next language period.)
- You did a good job the first time you wrote about Tom. Now you're going to write a perfect paper. Rewrite the whole story from the beginning. Write it so it doesn't have any mistakes.
- (After students complete their final draft, post the papers [and illustrations] of the story.)

Extension Lesson 83

Materials: Each student will need lined paper.

Objective A: Write a report about a specified topic.

Objective B: Rewrite [and illustrate] their report.

EXERCISE A

TOPICS

1. (Write on the board:)

   Someone I Would Like to Know Better

   - Here's the title for your story.
   - You're going to write about someone else you would like to know better. Maybe it is a movie star or somebody in sports. Maybe it is someone you have seen around your neighborhood or around school. You're going to name the person and give some reasons you would like to know that person better. You should tell what you find interesting about that person and what you would like to find out about that person. Tell at least three reasons.
   - Write your account. Raise your hand when you're finished.
     (Observe students and give feedback.)

2. (Call on different students to read their entire account. Praise parts that are good, and offer suggestions about organization, missing parts or parts that need work.)
3. (Collect papers. Mark mistakes in spelling and usage.)

EXERCISE B

REWRITING

- (Return papers during the next language period.)
- (Students are to write a final draft and possibly make an illustration for their account.)

Extension Lesson 84

Materials: Each student will need a copy of BLM 84 and lined paper.
Objective A: Write a multiparagraph story that infers and reports about a picture.
Objective B: Rewrite the story.

EXERCISE A
PASSAGE WRITING
VAGUE PICTURE

BLM 84

Write an interesting story about this picture.

- Tell what happened before the picture.
- Tell what happened in the picture.
- Tell what happened after the picture.
- You can write as many paragraphs as you want. Make your story interesting.

207

1. (Hand out BLM 84.)
- You're going to write an interesting story about the picture. You'll tell about what happened before the picture, what happened in the picture and what happened after the picture.
- Remember, first tell what happened before the picture. What do you tell first? (Signal.) *What happened before the picture.*
- What do you tell next? (Signal.) *What happened in the picture.*
  Yes, what happened in the picture. You'll tell what the boy and girl were thinking, feeling and doing.
- What will you tell last? (Signal.) *What happened after the picture.*

2. You can write as many paragraphs as you want. Make your story interesting. Raise your hand when you're finished. (Observe students and give feedback.)
3. (Call on different students to read their entire passage. Praise good parts. Offer suggestions about organization, missing parts or parts that need work.)
4. (Collect papers. Mark mistakes in spelling and usage.)

EXERCISE B
REWRITING

- (Return papers during the next language period. Students are to write a final draft and possibly make an illustration for their account.)

Extension Lesson 85

Materials: Each student will need lined paper.

Objective A: Write a report about a specified topic.

Objective B: Rewrite [and illustrate] their report.

EXERCISE A

TOPICS

1. (Write on the board:)

My Favorite TV Show

- Here's the title for your story.
- You're going to write about your favorite TV show. Remember, start out by naming the show. Tell about the things or the characters you like. You should give at least three reasons it's your favorite.
- Write your account. Raise your hand when you're finished.

(Observe students and give feedback.)

2. (Call on different students to read their entire account. Praise parts that are good, and offer suggestions about organization, missing parts or parts that need work.)
3. (Collect papers. Mark mistakes in spelling and usage.)

EXERCISE B

REWRITING

- (Return papers during the next language period.)
- (Students are to write a final draft and possibly make an illustration for their account.)

Extension Lesson 86

Materials: Each team will need a copy of BLM 86 and lined paper.

Objective: **Rewrite and rhyme paired prose.**

POEMS

BLM 86

Make a poem from this story.

STORY	POEM
There once was a king. Ring was his name.	• There once was a king. ______
He always carried so much gold that he looked elderly.	• He always carried so much gold. ______
The gold was so heavy he couldn't walk or stand up tall. Sometimes, he would have to crawl around.	• He couldn't stand up tall. ______
He was a terrible sight. He called in a doctor late one evening.	• He was a terrible sight. ______ ______
The doctor said his problem was he was carrying too much gold with him. So he weighed a lot, even though he was a slim man.	• The doctor said the king had too much gold on him. ______ ______
So the king left his gold at home after that night. And from then on, he could stand up the right way.	• The king left his gold at home after that night. ______ ______
Now his face is full of smiles. He can walk a long, long way.	• Now his face is full of smiles. ______

209

Note: For this activity, assign four students to each team. After forming groups, each team will make up its poem and read it to the rest of the class.

1. (Hand out BLM 86 to each team.)
- I'm going to read you a story. You're going to make up a poem from the story I tell you. This is a hard assignment. You'll have to think and do a lot of rewriting before you get your poem the way you want it.

2. I'll read the story. The poem you'll write will be a funny poem about a king. Here's a story about the king. Follow along:

> There once was a king. Ring was his name.
>
> He always carried so much gold that he looked elderly.
>
> The gold was so heavy he couldn't walk or stand up tall. Sometimes, he would have to crawl around.
>
> He was a terrible sight. He called in a doctor late one evening.
>
> The doctor said his problem was he was carrying too much gold with him. So he weighed a lot, even though he was a slim man.
>
> So the king left his gold at home after that night. And from then on, he could stand up the right way.
>
> Now his face is full of smiles. He can walk a long, long way.

3. The story doesn't have parts that rhyme, but some of the words are underlined. That means, you could use them as the last word in a line of the poem. The first part of what I read tells about the king's name and about his problem. What's the king's name? (Signal.) *Ring.*
- What's his problem? (Call on several students. Ideas: *He carried so much gold, he looked old. He couldn't do things.*)

- What were some of the things he couldn't do? (Call on several students. Ideas: *He couldn't stand up tall. He couldn't walk.*)

4. Listen. Start with this line: **There once was a king** and make up a line that rhymes. (Call on a student. Idea: *There once was a king. His name was [King]* ***Ring.***)
5. Listen. **He always carried so much gold that he looked elderly.** Start with **he always carried so much gold** and make up another ending that rhymes. (Call on a student. Idea: *He always carried so much gold* ***that he looked [like he was very] old.***)
6. Your group is to make up lines that rhyme for the whole story. Remember, after you write two lines that rhyme with each other, you write two more lines that rhyme with each other. The last two lines do not have to rhyme with the first two lines. When you get lines that you like, somebody in the group should write them down. Raise your hand when your group is finished writing the poem.
7. (Observe and give feedback to groups as they work. If groups get stuck on parts of the poem, prompt them about how to create a pair of lines that rhyme.)

Key:
There once was a king.
His name was ***Ring.***

He always carried so much gold
that he looked [very] ***old.***

The gold was so heavy he couldn't
stand up tall.
Sometimes he would [fall and] ***crawl.***

He was a terrible sight.
He called a doctor late one ***night.***

The doctor said the king had too
much gold on him.
He weighed a lot even though he was
slim.

The king left his gold at home after
that night.
From then on he could stand up ***right.***

Now his face is full of smiles.
He can walk for ***miles and miles.***

Note: Other rhymes are possible. Not all groups should make up the same poem.

- (Do not require the same measure for each pair of lines that rhyme. As long as the measure is the same for both lines within a pair, the poem is acceptable.)

8. Check to make sure your poem tells the whole story. Each member of your group is to copy the group's poem. Raise your hand when you're finished. (Observe students and give feedback.)
9. (Have each group read its poem to the entire class.)

- (You may require each group to memorize the group's poem and recite it to the class.)

Extension Lesson 87

Materials: Each student will need lined paper and illustrating materials.

Objective A: Write a report about a specified topic.

Objective B: Rewrite and illustrate their report.

EXERCISE A

TOPICS

1. (Write on the board:)

A Time Somebody Helped Me Out

- Here's the title for your story.
- You're going to write about a time you needed help and somebody helped you. Maybe you needed money. Maybe you needed help with something you were trying to do. Think about a time when somebody really helped you out of a bad spot.

2. Listen: First you'll tell when somebody helped you and where you were. Then tell why you needed help and who helped you. Tell what the person did and what happened. End your story by telling what happened later. Write your account. Raise your hand when you're finished.

   (Observe students and give feedback.)

3. (Call on different students to read their entire account. Give feedback about good parts and parts that have problems.)
4. (Collect papers and give feedback for changes. Mark sentences that do not have ending marks. Mark parts that do not tell what they are supposed to tell.)

EXERCISE B

REWRITING

- (Return papers during the next language period.)
- (Students are later to revise their papers and incorporate the changes you indicated. After students revise their reports, direct students to illustrate their reports with a picture that shows what happened. They may write labels for the people or things in the picture.)

Extension Lesson 88

Materials: Each team will need a copy of BLM 88 and lined paper.

Objective: Rewrite and rhyme paired prose.

POEMS

BLM 88

Make a poem from this story.

STORY	POEM
Cal was a big green duck. But Cal was not very lucky.	• Cal was a big green duck.
Things always went bad for Cal. Nobody wanted to be his friend.	• Things always went bad for Cal.
When Cal was around, things were never good. They never went the way they should go.	• When Cal was around, things were never good.
One day, there wasn't a cloud in the sky. As soon as Cal started to fly, clouds appeared all over.	• One day, there wasn't a cloud in the sky.
One duck said, "I'll make a bet. Before Cal lands, we'll all be covered with water."	• One duck said, "I'll make a bet. ____"
That duck was absolutely right. Everything was flooded before the night was over.	• That duck was absolutely right.

209

Note: For this activity, assign four students to each team. After forming groups, each team will make up its poem and read it to the rest of the class.

1. (Hand out BLM 88 to each team.)
- I'm going to read you a story. I'll read the first part today. You're going to make up a poem from the story I tell you. This is a hard assignment. You'll have to think and do a lot of rewriting before you get your poem the way you want it.
- I'll read the story. Follow along. This is the first part of the story:

> Cal was a big green duck. But Cal was not very lucky.
>
> Things always went bad for Cal. Nobody wanted to be his friend.
>
> When Cal was around, things were never good. They never went the way they should go.
>
> One day, there wasn't a cloud in the sky. As soon as Cal started to fly, clouds appeared all over.
>
> One duck said, "I'll make a bet. Before Cal lands, we'll all be covered with water."
>
> That duck was absolutely right. Everything was flooded before the night was over.

2. The first part of what I read tells about the duck and his problem. What's the duck's name? (Signal.) *Cal.*
- What's his problem? (Call on several students. Ideas: *He was not lucky. Things didn't go well when he was around.*)
- What was a bad thing that happened? (Call on several students. Ideas: *Flooding; clouds would appear.*)

3. Listen. Start with this line: **Cal was a big green duck** and make up a line that rhymes. (Call on a student. Idea: *Cal was a big green duck.* ***But Cal didn't have much luck.***)

4. Listen. Here's another line: **Things always went bad for Cal.** Start with that line and make up another line that rhymes. (Call on a student. Idea: *Things always went bad for Cal.* ***Nobody wanted to be his pal.***)
5. Listen. Here's another line: **When Cal was around, things were never good.** Start with that line and make up another line that rhymes. (Call on a student. Idea: *When Cal was around, things were never good.* ***They never went the way they should.***)
6. Your group is to make up lines that rhyme for the whole story. Remember, after you write two lines that rhyme with each other, you write two more lines that rhyme with each other. The last two lines do not have to rhyme with the first two lines. When you get lines that you like, somebody in the group should write them down. Raise your hand when your group is finished writing the poem.
7. (Observe and give feedback to groups as they work. If groups get stuck on parts of the poem, prompt them about how to create a pair of lines that rhyme.)

Key:

Cal was a big green duck.
But Cal didn't have much ***luck.***

Things always went bad for Cal.
Nobody wanted to be his ***pal.***

When Cal was around, things were never good.
They never went the way they ***should.***

One day, there wasn't a cloud in the sky.
But clouds appeared when Cal started to ***fly.***

One duck said, "I'll make a bet.
Before Cal lands, we'll all be ***wet.****"*

That duck was absolutely right.
Everything was flooded by the end of ***night.***

Note: Other rhymes are possible. Not all groups should make up the same poem.

- (Do not require the same measure for each pair of lines that rhyme. As long as the measure is the same for both lines within a pair, the poem is acceptable.)

8. Check to make sure your poem tells the whole story. Each member of your group is to copy the group's poem. Raise your hand when you're finished. (Observe students and give feedback.)
9. (Have each group read its poem to the entire class.)

- (You may require each group to memorize the group's poem and recite it to the class.)

Note: The other part of this poem is introduced in extension lesson 89.

Extension Lesson 89

Materials: Each team will need a copy of BLM 89 and lined paper.

Objective: Rewrite and rhyme paired prose.

POEMS

BLM 89

Make a poem from this story.

STORY	POEM
Nearby lived a goose that the ducks learned to hate. They thought she was mean, but she thought she was good.	• Nearby lived a goose that the ducks learned to hate.
The ducks said to Cal, "See if you can make that goose your friend."	• The ducks said to Cal,
Cal went over to the goose and just said, "Hi." As he spoke, an eagle came out of the air.	• Cal went over to the goose and just said, "Hi."
The goose saw the eagle and flew far away. And the ducks never saw her after that time.	• The goose saw the eagle and flew far away.
Cal told the others, "I couldn't make that goose my pal." Those ducks said, "But now a lot of ducks really love you, buddy."	• Cal told the others, "I couldn't make that goose my pal."

210

Note: For this activity, assign the same four-student teams.

1. (Hand out BLM 89 to each team.)
- You're going to write the second part of the poem about Cal. See what you remember about Cal. Was Cal lucky? (Signal.) *No.*
- If Cal wanted the weather to be sunny, what kind of weather would come in? (Call on a student. Idea: *Cloudy; rainy.*)
- If Cal tried to make friends with somebody, would he succeed? (Signal.) *No.*

2. I'll read the rest of the story. Follow along:

> Nearby lived a goose that the ducks learned to hate. They thought she was mean, but she thought she was good.
>
> The ducks said to Cal, "See if you can make that goose your friend."
>
> Cal went over to the goose and just said, "Hi." As he spoke, an eagle came out of the air.
>
> The goose saw the eagle and flew far away. And the ducks never saw her after that time.
>
> Cal told the others, "I couldn't make that goose my pal." Those ducks said, "But now a lot of ducks really love you, buddy."

3. Listen to the first line: **Nearby lived a goose that the ducks learned to hate.** Start with that line and make up another line that rhymes. (Call on a student. Idea: *Nearby lived a goose that the ducks learned to hate.* ***They thought she was mean, but she thought she was great.***)

4. Your group is to make up lines that rhyme for the whole story. Remember, after you write two lines that rhyme with each other, you write two more lines that rhyme with each other. The last two lines do not have to rhyme with the first two lines. When you get lines that you like, somebody in the group should write them down. Raise your hand when your group is finished writing the poem.

5. (Observe and give feedback to groups as they work. If groups get stuck on parts of the poem, prompt them about how to create a pair of lines that rhyme.)

> ***Key:***
> *Nearby lived a goose that the ducks learned to hate.*
> *They thought she was mean, but she thought she was* ***great.***
>
> *The ducks said to Cal,*
> *"See if you can make that goose your* ***pal."***
>
> *Cal went over to the goose and just said, "Hi."*
> *As he spoke, an eagle came out of the* ***sky.***
>
> *The goose saw the eagle and flew far away.*
> *And the ducks never saw her after that* ***day.***
>
> *Cal told the others, "I couldn't make that goose my pal."*
> *Those ducks said, "But now a lot of ducks really love you,* ***Cal."***

Note: Other rhymes are possible.

- (Do not require the same measure for each pair of lines that rhyme. As long as the measure is the same for both lines within a pair, the poem is acceptable.)

6. Check to make sure your poem tells the whole story. Each member of your group is to copy the group's poem. Raise your hand when you're finished. (Observe students and give feedback.)
7. (Have each group read its poem [part 2 or both parts] to the entire class.)

- (You may require each group to memorize the group's poem and recite it to the class.)

Extension Lesson 90

Materials: Each student will need a copy of BLM 90.

Objective: Locate and alphabetize words in a glossary.

GLOSSARY AND GUIDE WORDS

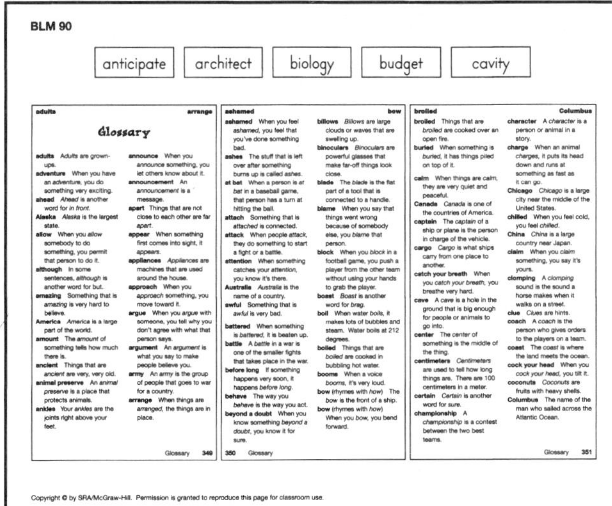

BLM 90

anticipate | architect | biology | budget | cavity

adults — **arrange**

Glossary

adults *Adults* are grown-ups.
adventure When you have an *adventure*, you do something very exciting.
ahead *Ahead* is another word for *in front*.
Alaska *Alaska* is the largest state.
allow When you *allow* somebody to do something, you permit that person to do it.
although In some sentences, *although* is another word for but.
amazing Something that is *amazing* is very hard to believe.
America *America* is a large part of the world.
amount The *amount* of something tells how much there is.
ancient Things that are *ancient* are very, very old.
animal preserve An *animal preserve* is a place that protects animals.
ankles Your *ankles* are the joints right above your feet.
announce When you *announce* something, you let others know about it.
announcement An *announcement* is a message.
apart Things that are not close to each other are far *apart*.
appear When something first comes into sight, it *appears*.
appliances *Appliances* are machines that are used around the house.
approach When you *approach* something, you move toward it.
argue When you *argue* with someone, you tell why you don't agree with what that person says.
argument An *argument* is what you say to make people believe you.
army An *army* is the group of people that goes to war for a country.
arrange When things are *arranged*, the things are in place.

Glossary 349

ashamed — **bow**

ashamed When you feel *ashamed*, you feel that you've done something bad.
ashes The stuff that is left over after something burns up is called *ashes*.
at bat When a person is *at bat* in a baseball game, that person has a turn at hitting the ball.
attach Something that is *attached* is connected.
attack When people *attack*, they do something to start a fight or a battle.
attention When something catches your *attention*, you know it's there.
Australia *Australia* is the name of a country.
awful Something that is *awful* is very bad.
battered When something is *battered*, it is beaten up.
battle A *battle* in a war is one of the smaller fights that takes place in the war.
before long If something happens very soon, it happens *before long*.
behave The way you *behave* is the way you act.
beyond a doubt When you know something *beyond a doubt*, you know it for sure.
billows *Billows* are large clouds or waves that are swelling up.
binoculars *Binoculars* are powerful glasses that make far-off things look close.
blade The *blade* is the flat part of a tool that is connected to a handle.
blame When you say that things went wrong because of somebody else, you *blame* that person.
block When you *block* in a football game, you push a player from the other team without using your hands to grab the player.
boast *Boast* is another word for *brag*.
boil When water *boils*, it makes lots of bubbles and steam. Water boils at 212 degrees.
boiled Things that are *boiled* are cooked in bubbling hot water.
booms When a voice *booms*, it's very loud.
bow (rhymes with *how*) The *bow* is the front of a ship.
bow (rhymes with *how*) When you *bow*, you bend forward.

350 Glossary

broiled — **Columbus**

broiled Things that are *broiled* are cooked over an open fire.
buried When something is *buried*, it has things piled on top of it.
calm When things are *calm*, they are very quiet and peaceful.
Canada *Canada* is one of the countries of America.
captain The *captain* of a ship or plane is the person in charge of the vehicle.
cargo *Cargo* is what ships carry from one place to another.
catch your breath When you *catch your breath*, you breathe very hard.
cave A *cave* is a hole in the ground that is big enough for people or animals to go into.
center The *center* of something is the middle of the thing.
centimeters *Centimeters* are used to tell how long things are. There are 100 centimeters in a meter.
certain *Certain* is another word for *sure*.
championship A *championship* is a contest between the two best teams.
character A *character* is a person or animal in a story.
charge When an animal *charges*, it puts its head down and runs at something as fast as it can go.
Chicago *Chicago* is a large city near the middle of the United States.
chilled When you feel cold, you feel *chilled*.
China *China* is a large country near Japan.
claim When you *claim* something, you say it's yours.
clomping A *clomping* sound is the sound a horse makes when it walks on a street.
clue *Clues* are hints.
coach A *coach* is the person who gives orders to the players on a team.
coast The *coast* is where the land meets the ocean.
cock your head When you *cock your head*, you tilt it.
coconuts *Coconuts* are fruits with heavy shells.
Columbus The name of the man who sailed across the Atlantic Ocean.

Glossary 351

1. (Hand out sample glossaries to the students [BLM 90].)
- Find page 349 in your glossary. ✔
2. Everybody, touch the first guide word on page 349. ✔
- What word? (Signal.) *Adults.*
- So what's the first word on page 349? (Signal.) *Adults.*
- Touch the other guide word for page 349. ✔
- Everybody, what's that guide word? (Signal.) *Arrange.*
- So what's the last word on page 349? (Signal.) *Arrange.*
3. Find page 351. ✔
- Page 351 has two guide words. Everybody, touch the first guide word on that page. ✔
- What's the first guide word? (Signal.) *Broiled.*
- So what's the first word on page 351? (Signal.) *Broiled.*
- What's the second guide word on page 351? (Signal.) *Columbus.*
- So what's the last word on that page? (Signal.) *Columbus.*
4. Touch the words in the boxes as I read them: anticipate, architect, biology, budget, cavity.
5. (Write on the board:)

biology

- Let's say I want to add the word **biology** to the glossary. Would I add **biology** to page 349 or to page 350 or to page 351? (Wait.) What page? (Signal.) *350.*
- Yes, **biology** comes between **ashamed** and **bow** in the alphabet.
6. Your turn. Find the word **biology** in the box at the top of your worksheet. ✔
- Now draw an arrow to show where the word **biology** would go in the glossary. Draw that arrow between two words. Raise your hand when you're finished. (Observe students and give feedback.)
- Everybody, name the word that comes just before where **biology** goes. (Signal.) *Binoculars.*
- Yes, **biology** comes between **binoculars** and **blade** in the alphabet.

7. Your turn. Draw arrows to show where the other boxed words would go in the glossary. Raise your hand when you're finished.
   (Observe students and give feedback.)
8. Everybody, name the word that comes just before where **anticipate** goes. (Signal.) *Announcement.*
   - Yes, **anticipate** comes between **announcement** and **apart.**
9. Everybody, name the word that comes just before where **architect** goes. (Signal.) *Approach.*
   - Yes, **architect** comes between **approach** and **argue** in the alphabet.
10. Everybody, name the word that comes just before where **budget** goes. (Signal.) *Broiled.*
    - Yes, **budget** comes between **broiled** and **buried** in the alphabet.
11. Everybody, name the word that comes just before where **cavity** goes. (Signal.) *Cave.*
    - Yes, **cavity** comes between **cave** and **center** in the alphabet.

Reproducible Blackline Masters

Table of Contents

corner	licking	floor	boy's hand	sitting

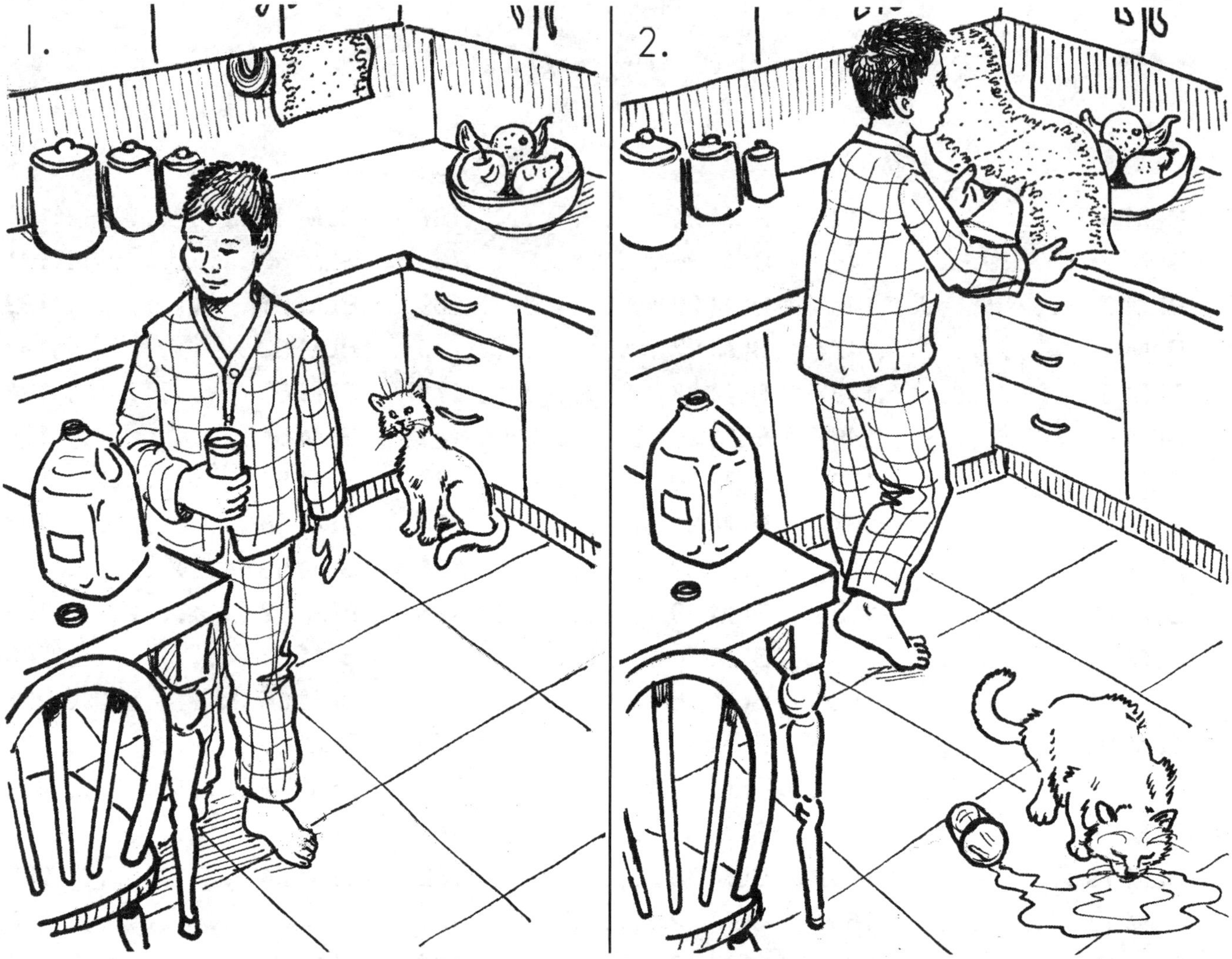

1.

2.

Write sentences that tell about the cat.

In picture 1, the cat is ______.

______.

Write sentences that tell about the glass.

In picture 1, the glass is ______.

______.

BLM 2

swinging	watching	outfield	ground
running	catching	girl's hands	glove

1. 2.

Write sentences that tell about the girl.

In picture 1, the girl is ____.

____.

Write sentences that tell about the boy.

In picture 1, the boy is ____.

____.

Write sentences that tell about the bat.

In picture 1, the bat is ____.

____.

reaching eat handing walking away
peel ground

1.

2.

Write sentences that tell about the monkey.

In picture 1, the monkey is ________________.
________________.

Write sentences that tell about the zookeeper.

In picture 1, the zookeeper is ________________.
________________.

Write sentences that tell about the banana.

In picture 1, the banana ________________.
________________.

lying	sitting	horse	ground	ready
bugle	horn	standing	running away	blow

1.

2.

Write sentences that tell about the man.

In picture 1, the man is ________.

________.

Write sentences that tell about the boy.

In picture 1, the boy is ________.

________.

Write sentences that tell about the horse.

In picture 1, the horse is ________.

________.

BLM 5

wagging	licking	running	ice cream cone	sidewalk

1.

2.

Write sentences that tell about the dog.

In picture 1, the dog is ____________.

____________.

Write sentences that tell about the girl.

In picture 1, the girl is ____________.

____________.

Write sentences that tell about the ball of ice cream.

In picture 1, the ball of ice cream is ____________.

____________.

BLM 6

Write four or more sentences that tell about everything that must have happened in the middle picture. Remember, tell about **the boy, the glass, the milk** and **the cat.**

floor	boy's hand	spilled	dropped	paper towels

BLM 7

Write four or more sentences that tell about everything that must have happened in the middle picture. Remember, tell about **the girl, the bat, the ball** and **the boy.**

toward	dropped	first base	glove

BLM 8

Write four or more sentences that tell about everything that must have happened in the middle picture. Remember, tell about **the monkey, the zookeeper** and **the banana.**

reaching   eat   handing   walking away   peel

BLM 9

Write four or more sentences that tell about everything that must have happened in the middle picture. Remember, tell about **the boy, the horse** and **the cowboy.**

1.

2.

3.

horn standing stared blew scared embarrassed

BLM 10

Write four or more sentences that tell about everything that must have happened in the middle picture. Remember, tell about **the dog, the girl** and **the ice cream.**

licked ice cream sidewalk jumped

BLM 11

Use the words below to make an alphabetical list.

great
carrot
top
horse
right
visit
elephant
north
jail
million

1. __________
2. __________
3. __________
4. __________
5. __________
6. __________
7. __________
8. __________
9. __________
10. __________

BLM 12

Use the words below to make an alphabetical list.

length raise bedroom should globe forest yellow umbrella desk whole

1. ______________________________
2. ______________________________
3. ______________________________
4. ______________________________
5. ______________________________
6. ______________________________
7. ______________________________
8. ______________________________
9. ______________________________
10. ______________________________

BLM 13

Use the words below to make an alphabetical list.

only
enter
answer
zoo
house
monkey
baby
don't
never
perfect

1. ______________________________

2. ______________________________

3. ______________________________

4. ______________________________

5. ______________________________

6. ______________________________

7. ______________________________

8. ______________________________

9. ______________________________

10. ______________________________

BLM 14

Use the words below to make an alphabetical list.

higher tongue ocean yourself insect unless funny question normal knocked

1. ______________________________
2. ______________________________
3. ______________________________
4. ______________________________
5. ______________________________
6. ______________________________
7. ______________________________
8. ______________________________
9. ______________________________
10. ______________________________

BLM 15

Use the words below to make an alphabetical list.

shovel
kitten
officer
argued
vacation
dance
usually
lifeboat
half
raindrop

1. ____________________

2. ____________________

3. ____________________

4. ____________________

5. ____________________

6. ____________________

7. ____________________

8. ____________________

9. ____________________

10. ____________________

BLM 16

Use the words below to make an alphabetical list.

label enormous rabbit voice captain unload decide peaceful middle forever

1. ______________________________

2. ______________________________

3. ______________________________

4. ______________________________

5. ______________________________

6. ______________________________

7. ______________________________

8. ______________________________

9. ______________________________

10. ______________________________

BLM 17

Use the words below to make an alphabetical list.

machine robin year peanut good bye vine holler zone water notice

1. ____________________
2. ____________________
3. ____________________
4. ____________________
5. ____________________
6. ____________________
7. ____________________
8. ____________________
9. ____________________
10. ____________________

BLM 18

Part A

coat
climb
canned
curly
crazy

Part B

Use the words below to make an alphabetical list.

mirror
myna
metal
money
machine

1. ______________________________

2. ______________________________

3. ______________________________

4. ______________________________

5. ______________________________

BLM 19

Underline the second letter in each word. Then write the words in alphabetical order.

oven once officer ocean outfit

1. ______________________

2. ______________________

3. ______________________

4. ______________________

5. ______________________

BLM 20

Underline the second letter in each word. Then write the words in alphabetical order.

swallow
squirrel
steady
scale
second
solid
smelly
shelves

1. ______________________________

2. ______________________________

3. ______________________________

4. ______________________________

5. ______________________________

6. ______________________________

7. ______________________________

8. ______________________________

BLM 21

Underline the second letter in each word. Then write the words in alphabetical order.

boast building blew breath beyond billows

1. ______________________________

2. ______________________________

3. ______________________________

4. ______________________________

5. ______________________________

6. ______________________________

BLM 22

Underline the second letter in each word. Then write the words in alphabetical order.

eraser
enormous
edge
easy
evening
escape
eggs
eyes

1. ______________________________

2. ______________________________

3. ______________________________

4. ______________________________

5. ______________________________

6. ______________________________

7. ______________________________

8. ______________________________

change
cabbage
dollar
coast
decide
dream
circus

1. ______________________________

2. ______________________________

3. ______________________________

4. ______________________________

5. ______________________________

6. ______________________________

7. ______________________________

BLM 24

trouble
thought
ruler
tenth
rich
twice
taste
rough
return

1. ______________________________

2. ______________________________

3. ______________________________

4. ______________________________

5. ______________________________

6. ______________________________

7. ______________________________

8. ______________________________

9. ______________________________

middle
island
machine
insist
mummy
money
idea

1. ______________________________

2. ______________________________

3. ______________________________

4. ______________________________

5. ______________________________

6. ______________________________

7. ______________________________

BLM 26

flower
juggle
football
fence
fifty
join

1. ____________________

2. ____________________

3. ____________________

4. ____________________

5. ____________________

6. ____________________

thirsty
notice
twice
terrible
neither
traffic
toast

1. ______________________________
2. ______________________________
3. ______________________________
4. ______________________________
5. ______________________________
6. ______________________________
7. ______________________________

balloon
lucky
blood
brave
ledge
busy
liar
bench

1. ______________________________

2. ______________________________

3. ______________________________

4. ______________________________

5. ______________________________

6. ______________________________

7. ______________________________

8. ______________________________

ruler
airplane
done
knives
thumb
dinner
ceiling
report
honest
weather

1. ______________________________

2. ______________________________

3. ______________________________

4. ______________________________

5. ______________________________

6. ______________________________

7. ______________________________

8. ______________________________

9. ______________________________

10. ______________________________

BLM 30

banana
plastic
electric
people
special
early
amaze
hundred
decide
purple

1. __________

2. __________

3. __________

4. __________

5. __________

6. __________

7. __________

8. __________

9. __________

10. __________

BLM 31

shadow lemon giant visit destroy great younger bread space globe

1. ____
2. ____
3. ____
4. ____
5. ____
6. ____
7. ____
8. ____
9. ____
10. ____

count
collar
complete
cob
cod
coat
cone
cook

1. ____________________

2. ____________________

3. ____________________

4. ____________________

5. ____________________

6. ____________________

7. ____________________

8. ____________________

dry
driver
draft
dream
drop
drum

1. ____________________

2. ____________________

3. ____________________

4. ____________________

5. ____________________

6. ____________________

cent		**cops**
	can	
	certain	
	cup	
	chip	
	circus	
	clipper	
	call	
	city	

1. ______________________________

2. ______________________________

3. ______________________________

4. ______________________________

5. ______________________________

BLM 35

chief		**clean**
	circle	
	chill	
	chew	
	chirp	
	copy	
	chin	
	chunk	
	class	
	claw	

1. ______________________________

2. ______________________________

3. ______________________________

4. ______________________________

5. ______________________________

6. ______________________________

7. ______________________________

Glossary

adults *Adults* are grown-ups.

adventure When you have an *adventure,* you do something very exciting.

ahead *Ahead* is another word for *in front.*

Alaska *Alaska* is the largest state.

allow When you *allow* somebody to do something, you permit that person to do it.

although In some sentences, *although* is another word for *but.*

amazing Something that is *amazing* is very hard to believe.

America *America* is a large part of the world.

amount The *amount* of something tells how much there is.

ancient Things that are *ancient* are very, very old.

animal preserve An *animal preserve* is a place that protects animals.

ankles Your *ankles* are the joints right above your feet.

announce When you *announce* something, you let others know about it.

announcement An *announcement* is a message.

apart Things that are not close to each other are far *apart*.

appear When something first comes into sight, it *appears*.

appliances *Appliances* are machines that are used around the house.

approach When you *approach* something, you move toward it.

argue When you *argue* with someone, you tell why you don't agree with what that person says.

argument An *argument* is what you say to make people believe you.

army An *army* is the group of people that goes to war for a country.

arrange When things are *arranged,* the things are in place.

ashamed When you feel *ashamed,* you feel that you've done something bad.

ashes The stuff that is left over after something burns up is called *ashes*.

at bat When a person is *at bat* in a baseball game, that person has a turn at hitting the ball.

attach Something that is *attached* is connected.

attack When people *attack,* they do something to start a fight or a battle.

attention When something catches your *attention,* you know it's there.

Australia *Australia* is the name of a country.

awful Something that is *awful* is very bad.

battered When something is *battered,* it is beaten up.

battle A *battle* in a war is one of the smaller fights that takes place in the war.

before long If something happens very soon, it happens *before long*.

behave The way you *behave* is the way you act.

beyond a doubt When you know something *beyond a doubt*, you know it for sure.

billows *Billows* are large clouds or waves that are swelling up.

binoculars *Binoculars* are powerful glasses that make far-off things look close.

blade The *blade* is the flat part of a tool that is connected to a handle.

blame When you say that things went wrong because of somebody else, you *blame* that person.

block When you *block* in a football game, you push a player from the other team without using your hands to grab the player.

boast *Boast* is another word for *brag.*

boil When water *boils,* it makes lots of bubbles and steam. Water boils at 212 degrees.

boiled Things that are *boiled* are cooked in bubbling hot water.

booms When a voice *booms,* it's very loud.

bow (rhymes with *how*) The *bow* is the front of a ship.

bow (rhymes with *how*) When you *bow,* you bend forward.

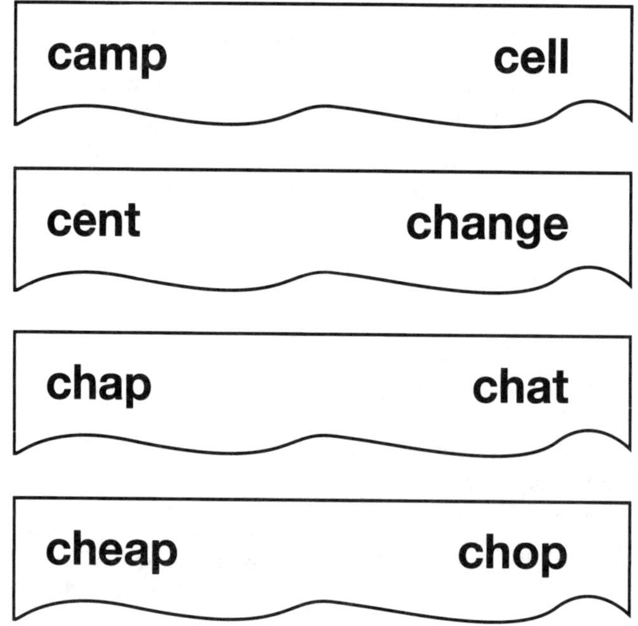

1. cat ______________________________
2. chest ______________________________
3. chart ______________________________
4. care ______________________________
5. chair ______________________________
6. chase ______________________________

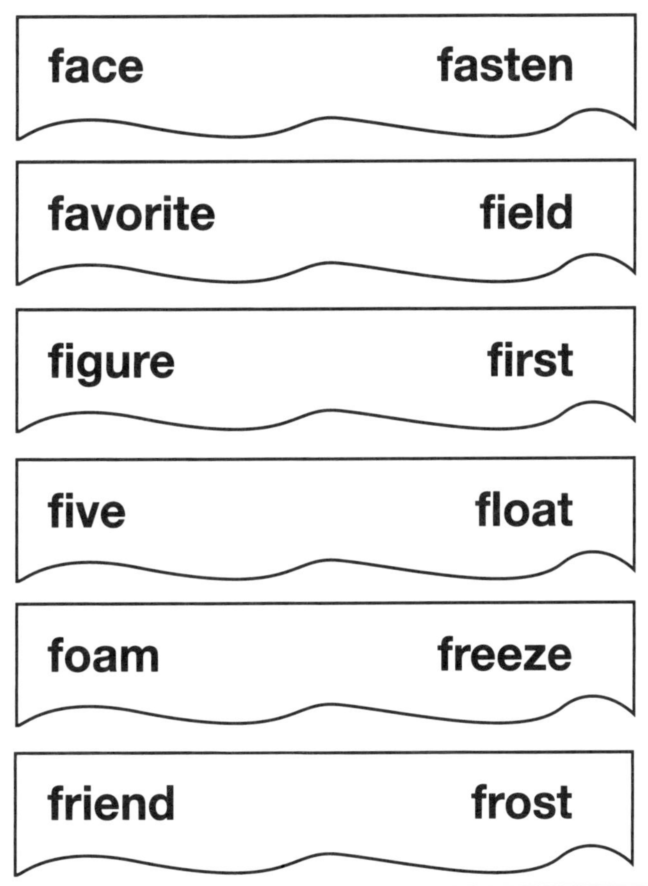

1. frond ______________________
2. fever ______________________
3. famous ______________________
4. flea ______________________
5. factory ______________________
6. finally ______________________
7. forest ______________________
8. faint ______________________
9. frisky ______________________
10. finish ______________________

BLM 38

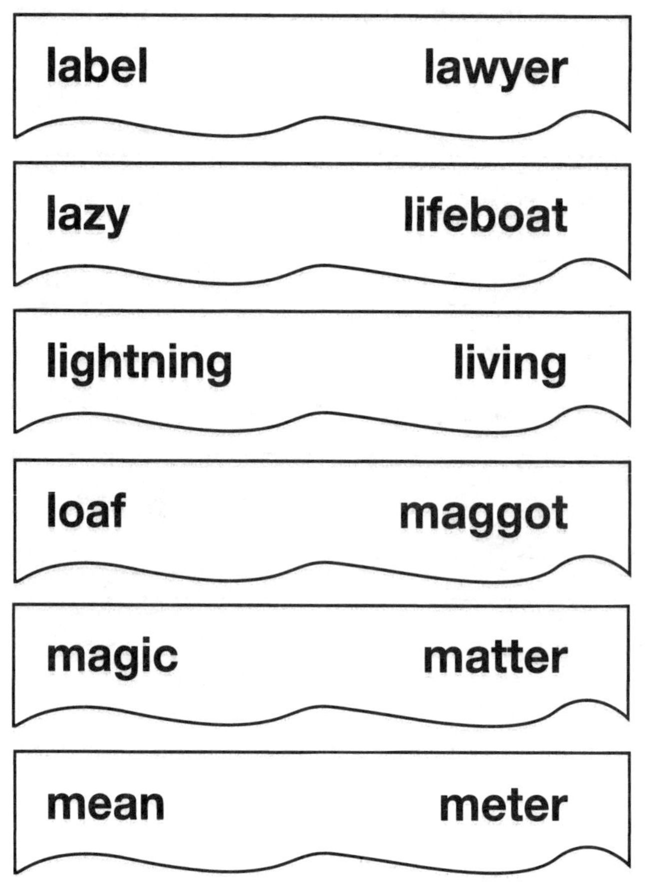

1. metal ______________________
2. list ______________________
3. ledge ______________________
4. machine ______________________
5. lady ______________________
6. manage ______________________
7. learn ______________________
8. laughter ______________________
9. league ______________________
10. lucky ______________________

BLM 42

Write the words in the box in alphabetical order.

fear koala thirty fence ceiling thaw tough leopard

1. ______________________________

2. ______________________________

3. ______________________________

4. ______________________________

5. ______________________________

6. ______________________________

7. ______________________________

8. ______________________________

Write the guide words for the page where you would find that word in a glossary.

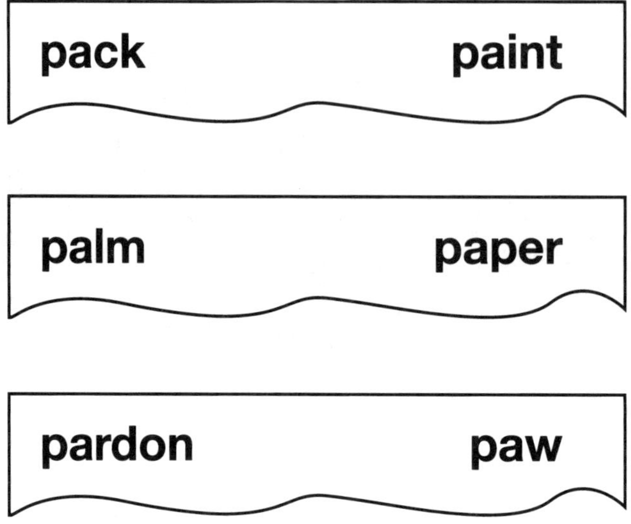

1. pass ______________________________

2. page ______________________________

3. patch ______________________________

4. panel ______________________________

BLM 44

Write the words in the box in alphabetical order.

church measure family came palace image breath special close million

1. ______________________________

2. ______________________________

3. ______________________________

4. ______________________________

5. ______________________________

6. ______________________________

7. ______________________________

8. ______________________________

9. ______________________________

10. ______________________________

BLM 45

Write directions for making the figure.

below square capital above

BLM 46

Write directions for making the figure.

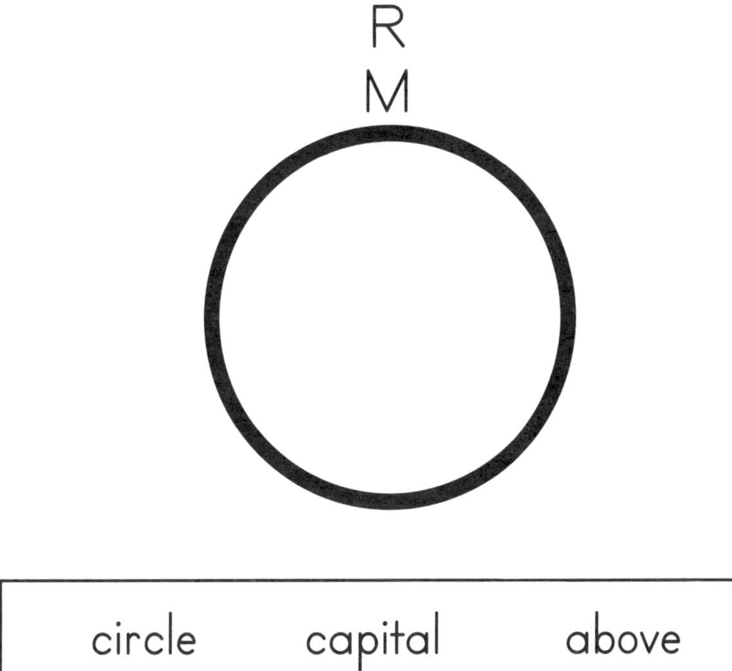

BLM 47

Write directions for making the figure.

triangle	square	capital	middle

BLM 48

Write directions for making the figure.

below	capital

BLM 49

Write directions for making the figure.

triangle	middle	capital

BLM 50

Write directions for making the figure.

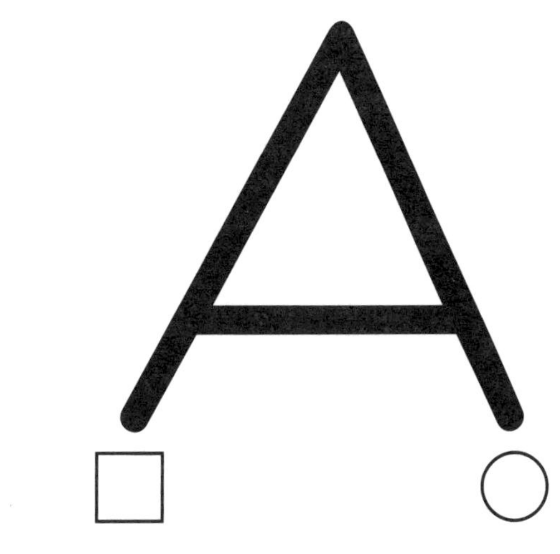

square	circle	below

BLM 51

Write directions for making the figure.

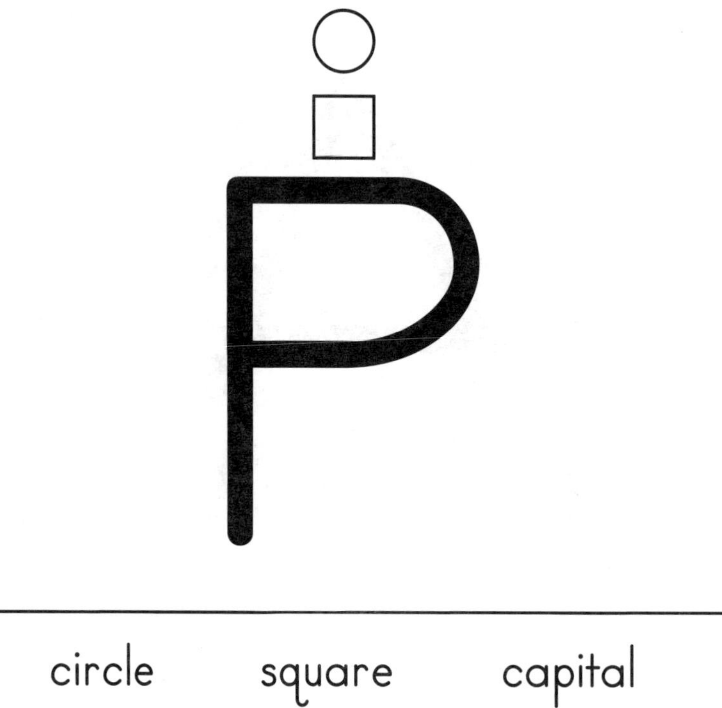

BLM 52

Write directions for making the figure.

A B

horizontal	middle	below	end

BLM 53

Write directions for making the figure.

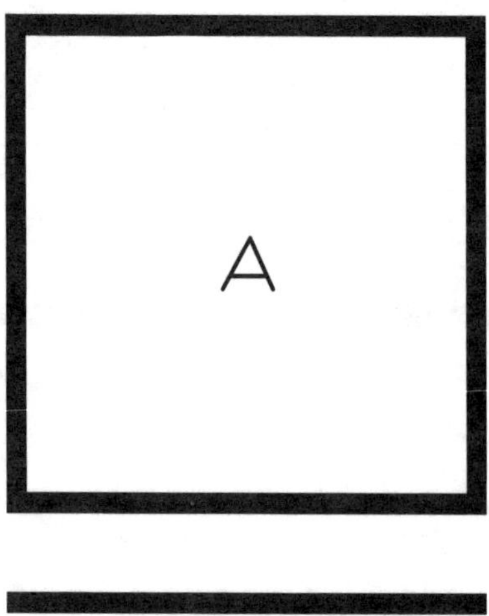

horizontal side square below

BLM 54

Write directions for making the figure.

square	above	horizontal	edge

BLM 57

Write about a person you admire.

Why I Admire ____________

A person I really admire is (tell who) ____________.

I admire ____________ because (tell why) ____________.

One time (tell something the person did that you admire) ____________
____________.

Another time (tell something else the person did that you admire) ____________
____________.

I hope (tell what you hope about that person) ____________
____
____________.

BLM 58

Write about jobs you would like.

Jobs I Would Like

When I grow up, I would like to be a ______ or a ______.

Here are the reasons I would like to be a ______.

One reason is ______.

Another reason is ______.

Here are the reasons I would like to be a ______.

One reason is ______.

Another reason is ______.

BLM 59

Write an interesting story about this picture.

- Tell what happened before the picture.
- Tell what happened in the picture.
- Tell what happened after the picture.
- You can write as many paragraphs as you want.
  Make your story interesting.

BLM 62

Write about a time you did something that was really good.

Something Really Good

I did something really good (tell when) ______________________________.

I was (tell where) ______________________________.

I was there because (tell why) ______________________________

______________________________.

(Tell what happened. Tell what you did that was good. Tell all the important things.) ______________________________

____

____

Write about something you did that you are sorry about.

Something I Am Sorry About

I did something that I felt really sorry about (tell when) ______________________.

I was (tell where) ______________________.

I was there because (tell why) ______________________.

If I could do it again, I would (tell what you would do) ______________________.

My Best Friend

My best friend is (tell who) ________.
Here are three things I really like about (tell who):

1. One thing I really like about my friend is ________.
2. Another thing I really like about my friend is ________.
3. Another thing I really like about my friend is ________.

I hope (write what you hope about yourself and this person) ________.

BLM 66

Write an interesting story about this picture.

- Tell what happened before the picture.
- Tell what happened in the picture.
- Tell what happened after the picture.
- You can write as many paragraphs as you want.
  Make your story interesting.

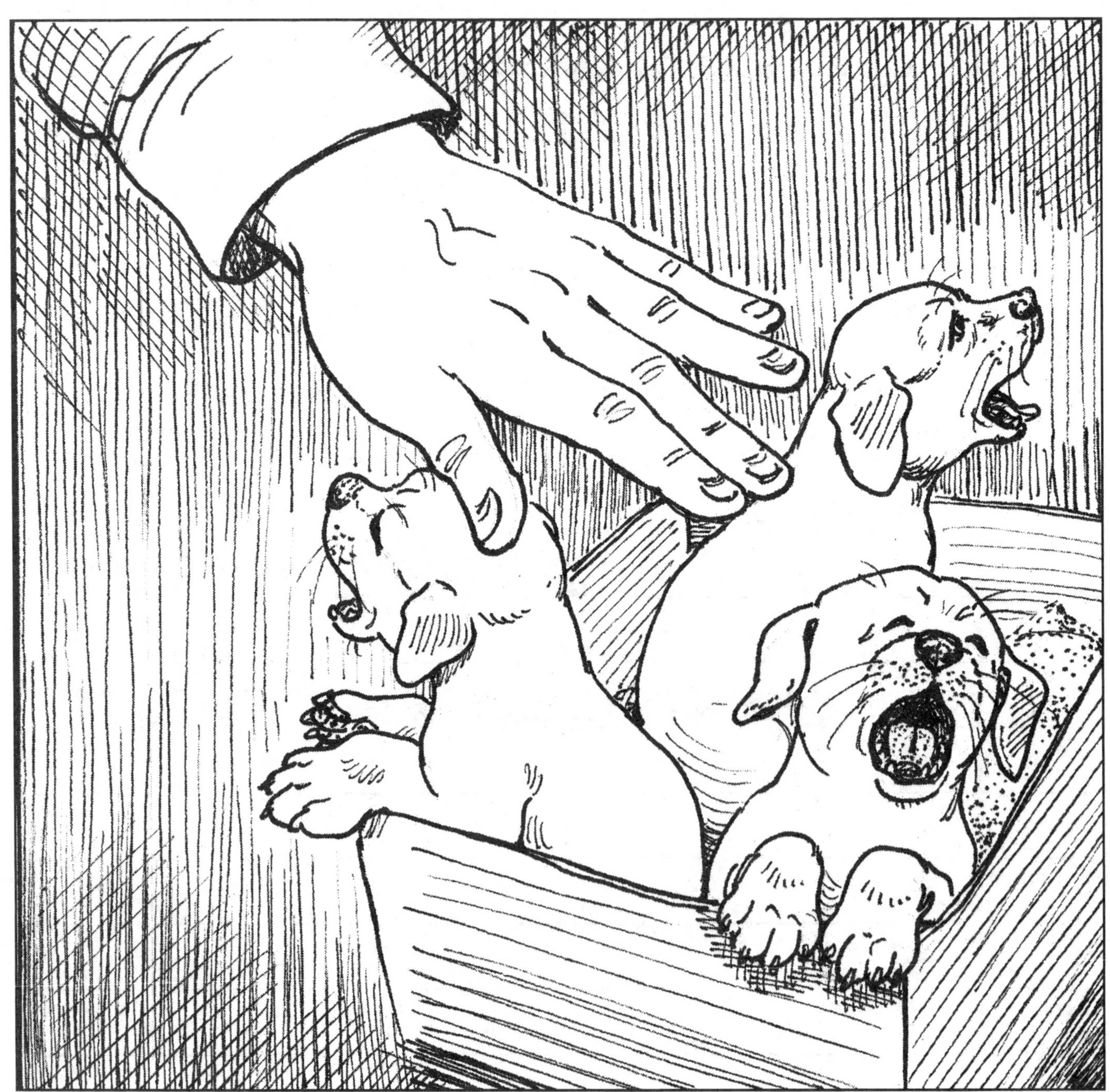

What I Worked On in School Yesterday

Here are the subjects I worked on yesterday: (tell subjects)

Here are some of the things we did during reading. (Tell about two or more things that happened during reading.)

Here are some of the things we did during math. (Tell about two or more things that happened during math.)

Here are some of the things we did during (name another subject) (Tell about two or more things that happened during that subject.)

Someone I Would Like to Know Better

One reason I would like to know (name of person) better is (tell reason).

Another reason I would like to know (name of person) better is (tell reason).

A third reason I would like to know (name of person) better is (tell reason).

I hope (write your ending) (Tell what you hope and what you will do.)

BLM 74

Write an interesting story about this picture.

- Tell what happened before the picture.
- Tell what happened in the picture.
- Tell what happened after the picture.
- You can write as many paragraphs as you want.
  Make your story interesting.

BLM 80

Write an interesting story about this picture.

- Tell what happened before the picture.
- Tell what happened in the picture.
- Tell what happened after the picture.
- You can write as many paragraphs as you want.
  Make your story interesting.

BLM 84

Write an interesting story about this picture.

- Tell what happened before the picture.
- Tell what happened in the picture.
- Tell what happened after the picture.
- You can write as many paragraphs as you want.
  Make your story interesting.

BLM 86

Make a poem from this story.

STORY	POEM
There once was a king. Ring was his name.	• There once was a king. ____________________
He always carried so much gold that he looked elderly.	• He always carried so much gold. ____________________
The gold was so heavy he couldn't walk or stand up tall. Sometimes, he would have to crawl around.	• He couldn't stand up tall. ____________________
He was a terrible sight. He called in a doctor late one evening.	• He was a terrible sight. ____________________ ____________________
The doctor said his problem was he was carrying too much gold with him. So he weighed a lot, even though he was a slim man.	• The doctor said the king had too much gold on him. ____________________ ____________________
So the king left his gold at home after that night. And from then on, he could stand up the right way.	• The king left his gold at home after that night. ____________________ ____________________
Now his face is full of smiles. He can walk a long, long way.	• Now his face is full of smiles. ____________________

BLM 88

Make a poem from this story.

STORY	POEM
Cal was a big green duck. But Cal was not very lucky.	• Cal was a big green duck. ____________________ ____________________
Things always went bad for Cal. Nobody wanted to be his friend.	• Things always went bad for Cal. ____________________ ____________________
When Cal was around, things were never good. They never went the way they should go.	• When Cal was around, things were never good. ____________________ ____________________
One day, there wasn't a cloud in the sky. As soon as Cal started to fly, clouds appeared all over.	• One day, there wasn't a cloud in the sky. ____________________ ____________________
One duck said, "I'll make a bet. Before Cal lands, we'll all be covered with water."	• One duck said, "I'll make a bet. ____________________ ____________________"
That duck was absolutely right. Everything was flooded before the night was over.	• That duck was absolutely right. ____________________ ____________________

BLM 89

Make a poem from this story.

STORY	POEM
Nearby lived a goose that the ducks learned to hate. They thought she was mean, but she thought she was good.	• Nearby lived a goose that the ducks learned to hate. ________________ ________________
The ducks said to Cal, "See if you can make that goose your friend."	• The ducks said to Cal, ________________ ________________
Cal went over to the goose and just said, "Hi." As he spoke, an eagle came out of the air.	• Cal went over to the goose and just said, "Hi." ________________ ________________
The goose saw the eagle and flew far away. And the ducks never saw her after that time.	• The goose saw the eagle and flew far away. ________________ ________________
Cal told the others, "I couldn't make that goose my pal." Those ducks said, "But now a lot of ducks really love you, buddy."	• Cal told the others, "I couldn't make that goose my pal." ________________ ________________ ________________

BLM 90

anticipate | architect | biology | budget | cavity

Glossary

adults *Adults* are grown-ups.
adventure When you have an *adventure,* you do something very exciting.
ahead *Ahead* is another word for *in front.*
Alaska *Alaska* is the largest state.
allow When you *allow* somebody to do something, you permit that person to do it.
although In some sentences, *although* is another word for but.
amazing Something that is *amazing* is very hard to believe.
America *America* is a large part of the world.
amount The *amount* of something tells how much there is.
ancient Things that are *ancient* are very, very old.
animal preserve An *animal preserve* is a place that protects animals.
ankles Your *ankles* are the joints right above your feet.
announce When you *announce* something, you let others know about it.
announcement An *announcement* is a message.
apart Things that are not close to each other are far *apart.*
appear When something first comes into sight, it *appears.*
appliances *Appliances* are machines that are used around the house.
approach When you *approach* something, you move toward it.
argue When you *argue* with someone, you tell why you don't agree with what that person says.
argument An *argument* is what you say to make people believe you.
army An *army* is the group of people that goes to war for a country.
arrange When things are *arranged,* the things are in place.

ashamed When you feel *ashamed,* you feel that you've done something bad.
ashes The stuff that is left over after something burns up is called *ashes.*
at bat When a person is *at bat* in a baseball game, that person has a turn at hitting the ball.
attach Something that is *attached* is connected.
attack When people *attack,* they do something to start a fight or a battle.
attention When something catches your *attention,* you know it's there.
Australia *Australia* is the name of a country.
awful Something that is *awful* is very bad.
battered When something is *battered,* it is beaten up.
battle A *battle* in a war is one of the smaller fights that takes place in the war.
before long If something happens very soon, it happens *before long.*
behave The way you *behave* is the way you act.
beyond a doubt When you know something *beyond a doubt*, you know it for sure.
billows *Billows* are large clouds or waves that are swelling up.
binoculars *Binoculars* are powerful glasses that make far-off things look close.
blade The *blade* is the flat part of a tool that is connected to a handle.
blame When you say that things went wrong because of somebody else, you *blame* that person.
block When you *block* in a football game, you push a player from the other team without using your hands to grab the player.
boast *Boast* is another word for *brag.*
boil When water *boils,* it makes lots of bubbles and steam. Water boils at 212 degrees.
boiled Things that are *boiled* are cooked in bubbling hot water.
booms When a voice *booms,* it's very loud.
bow (rhymes with *how*) The *bow* is the front of a ship.
bow (rhymes with *how*) When you *bow,* you bend forward.

broiled Things that are *broiled* are cooked over an open fire.
buried When something is *buried,* it has things piled on top of it.
calm When things are *calm,* they are very quiet and peaceful.
Canada *Canada* is one of the countries of America.
captain The *captain* of a ship or plane is the person in charge of the vehicle.
cargo *Cargo* is what ships carry from one place to another.
catch your breath When you *catch your breath,* you breathe very hard.
cave A *cave* is a hole in the ground that is big enough for people or animals to go into.
center The *center* of something is the middle of the thing.
centimeters *Centimeters* are used to tell how long things are. There are 100 centimeters in a meter.
certain *Certain* is another word for *sure.*
championship A *championship* is a contest between the two best teams.
character A *character* is a person or animal in a story.
charge When an animal *charges,* it puts its head down and runs at something as fast as it can go.
Chicago *Chicago* is a large city near the middle of the United States.
chilled When you feel cold, you feel *chilled.*
China *China* is a large country near Japan.
claim When you *claim* something, you say it's yours.
clomping A *clomping* sound is the sound a horse makes when it walks on a street.
clue *Clues* are hints.
coach A *coach* is the person who gives orders to the players on a team.
coast The *coast* is where the land meets the ocean.
cock your head When you *cock your head,* you tilt it.
coconuts *Coconuts* are fruits with heavy shells.
Columbus The name of the man who sailed across the Atlantic Ocean.